WEATHER

WEATHER

THE ULTIMATE BOOK OF METEOROLOGICAL EVENTS

FOREWORD BY DR. D. JAMES BAKER

FROM THE CONTRIBUTORS OF THE *WEATHER GUIDE CALENDAR*

ACCORD PUBLISHING
a division of Andrews McMeel Publishing, LLC

Weather: The Ultimate Book of Meteorological Events
Copyright © 2007 by Accord Publishing
Photography credits and copyrights page 254.
For information, write Accord Publishing, a division of
Andrews McMeel Publishing, LLC,
1404 Larimer Street, Suite 200, Denver, CO 80202

Packaged by Jennifer Barry Design, Fairfax, CA
Design and editing: Jennifer Barry
Layout production: Kristen Hall
Text editor: Blake Hallanan
Photography coordinator: Laura Del Fava
Foreword by D. James Baker
Essays on pp. 27, 57, 93, 133, and 185 by Walter Lyons, CCM

Printed in China

07 08 09 10 11 WKT 10 9 8 7 6 5 4 3 2 1

ISBN-13: 978-0-7407-6989-4
ISBN-10: 0-7407-6989-8

Library of Congress Cataloging-in-Publication Data:

Weather : the ultimate book of meterological events / from the
contributors of the Weather Guide Calendar.
        p. cm.
    Includes bibliographical references and index.
    ISBN-13: 978-0-7407-6989-4 (alk. paper)
    ISBN-10: 0-7407-6989-8 (alk. paper)
1. Weather—Popular works. 2. Meteorology—Popular works.

    QC981.2.W47 2007
    551.5—dc22   2007038988

Attention: Schools and Businesses
Andrews McMeel books are available at quantity discounts with
bulk purchase for educational, business, or sales promotional use.
For information, please write to:
Special Sales Department, Andrews McMeel Publishing, LLC,
4520 Main Street, Kansas City, Missouri 64111

www.andrewsmcmeel.com

LEFT: *A supercell thunderstorm produced this cloud-to-ground bolt of lightning at sunset near Medicine Lodge, Kansas. The severe storm dropped baseball-sized hail before losing its flying saucer-like shape. Supercells are generated by rotating, rising columns of air called "mesocyclones" that can give parts of the clouds a corkscrew shape. The warm air rises at speeds up to 170 mph accounting for the hard, cauliflower-like appearance of supercells, which can last for hours and move great distances. Photo: Jim Reed/Getty Images*

ABOVE: *This F3 tornado, with winds up to 200 mph, touched down in rural South Dakota, near Aberdeen. Not more than 5 seconds after this shot was taken, the tornado destroyed the farm in the foreground. Photo Courtesy of NOAA*

LEFT: *It is nearly a cliché that tornadoes target trailer parks. While there is no deliberate intent on the part of nature, mobile homes certainly are at risk. This twister is in the process of demolishing a mobile home near Spring Valley, Texas. It was the first of at least eight tornadoes that menaced central Texas on this day (May 27, 1997), which killed 27 people in the town of Jarrell. Photo: Lon Curtis*

RIGHT: *This classic, anvil-shaped, single-cell thunderstorm dumped rain and threw lightning over Tuscon, Arizona, in September, 1983. The silhouettes seen in the foreground are two people who were enjoying the show at twilight. Photo: A. T. Willett*

NORTH AMERICAN STORM TRACKS

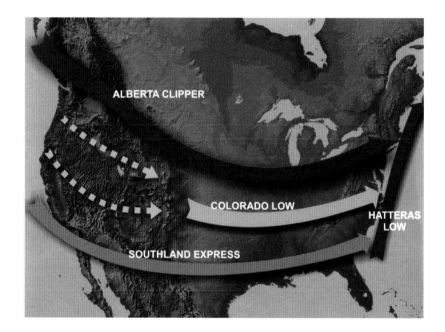

With a canopy of dark clouds overhead, the South Rim of the Grand Canyon provided a magnificent target as it was by the crackle of intense cloud-to-ground lightning. Monsoon rains, always needed in this arid part of the Colorado Plateau, followed this shadow of lightning captured from Point Sublime on the North Rim. Photo: Dick Dietrich/Dietrich Stock Photos

In some parts of the country, it seems that storms follow the same paths most of the time, almost as if they were following an invisible itinerary. This is not a case of flaky observation; many local storms, particularly in hilly or mountainous geography, are spawned and directed in part from the influence of terrain. In the Front Range of the Rocky Mountains of Colorado, for example, summer thunderstorms are often prevalent along certain northeasterly paths. A local weather forecaster was once made notorious for predicting a successful—as in rain-free—outdoor event, but only if it were held at one end of a city park and not the other.

Larger storm systems and fronts are also influenced by geography. Driven by the conditions associated with large bodies of water, ocean currents, mountain barriers, and seasonal jet stream patterns, the United States can be said to have four major storm tracks. These may vary from year to year—and from season to season—but they represent a general, known pattern upon which regional and local weather forecasters may rely, at least for historical comparison.

In the north, the Alberta clipper is a well-recognized presence, often identified in media headlines attached to weather changes. Not surprisingly, this storm track gets its name from the Canadian province of Alberta, where it seems to originate. However, the clipper actually arises in the northern Pacific Ocean and, linked to the jet stream, drops its initial load of moisture as it shifts up and over the mountainous barrier it encounters in coastal British Columbia. Flowing eastward over additional mountains in Alberta, the now-drier clipper typically collides with the cold air mass often stationed—and stationary—over the western Canadian plains. High-pressure systems centered to the north can push the flowing clipper southward, producing major winter storms in the northern United States and Great Plains; otherwise, it heads more or less easterly across Canada.

Although most Alberta clippers are accompanied by some moisture, they are not usually known for heavy snowfall unless they interact with other storms pulling moisture up from the Gulf of Mexico. Characteristics of a typical Alberta clipper include harsh winds and sharp drops in temperature, as much as

33

30 degrees Fahrenheit (16 degrees Celsius) in less than 12 hours. Clippers are common throughout the year, but they are coldest and most damaging in winter months. They can come at a rapid pace, one or two a week for several weeks in a row.

In the center part of the country, the major storm system is the Colorado low, which appears to pop up in southeastern Colorado. It is sometimes referred to as the Colorado-Trinidad low, because an apparent point of origin may be the town of Trinidad, near the southern border of the state. Such a storm track may also originate even farther south, in northern New Mexico. The Colorado low typically starts as a low-pressure mass and moves east to northeast, sometimes affecting cities as far north as Chicago. Usually it produces heavy winter precipitation as far east as the Atlantic coast. In the winter, Colorado lows can be pushed down by the jet stream or blocking air masses to the north, and can bring icy conditions and heavy snow as far south as Texas, where these storms are traditionally called blue northers.

Although most pronounced during winter months, when they can produce prodigious, wide-ranging blizzards—Colorado lows produce most of the Midwest's snow—this storm track also sweeps through the Midwest in the summer, pushing thunderstorms and widespread rain ahead of a cold front. At an extreme, a summer Colorado low can bring heavy thunderstorms that linger for several hours over an affected area.

To the south, the Southland express produces the most recognizable storm track as it moves across the country. Originating in the Pacific Ocean waters off northern California, it sweeps down and crosses land in the southern part of the state, driving eastward toward Florida and the Atlantic. As it crosses the Gulf states, it can be affected by moisture from the Gulf of Mexico, as well as fronts to the north. The Southland express is also referred to as a Gulf coaster, particularly when it pushes low across the Gulf states and Gulf of Mexico. When it blows through, it is known for severe weather, particularly heavy rainfall—snow when freezing temperatures coincide—and it can push upward into the Midwest and East Coast states.

The fourth major storm track affecting the United States is called the Hatteras low. Linked to the area around Cape Hatteras, off the North Carolina coast, a typical outcome for this system is to push up along the Atlantic coast; in New England, the Hatteras low is also known as a nor'easter. This name originated in colonial days, when weather observers named storms for the direction from which the wind was blowing. Even though the Hatteras low is moving to, not coming from, the northeast, its counterclockwise movement makes it appear just the opposite.

Capable of producing some of the most intense storm conditions, the Hatteras low is sometimes referred to as a "bomb" cyclone. Cyclone because the air moves counterclockwise (like all North American storm tracks); bomb because such a storm can develop very quickly. The warm water of the Gulf Stream lies next to the colder waters of the Atlantic coast, a situation ripe for extreme weather and generating heavy rain—or snow in wintry conditions—as far north as the Maritime provinces in Canada. At their worst, Hatteras lows produce extreme weather both on land and at sea. "The Perfect Storm" of best-seller book fame (as well as the blockbuster movie version) was a Hatteras low.

These four major tracks are mostly independent of one another but, under some circumstances, can combine or collide, dramatically increasing their stormy potential. In November, for example, the Great Lakes region can provide a target zone where an Alberta clipper and a Colorado low converge, their effects made more severe by the plentiful supply of moisture—and source of heat—represented by the Great Lakes. At least 25 "killer storms" have been recorded on the Great Lakes in November, producing more deaths from shipwrecks in that month than at any other time of year.

—*Kim Long*

TORNADO FORECASTING:
A BRIEF HISTORY

Although Benjamin Franklin realized as early as 1743 that storms in the United States generally moved from west to east or southwest to northeast, the lack of rapid communications at the time hindered warning regions in a storm's path. It was not until a century later, when the first commercial telegraph line was opened on April 1, 1845, that forewarning communities of approaching severe storms and tornadoes was possible.

Joseph Henry, America's premier physicist and the first director of the Smithsonian Institution, proposed in a letter to the Smithsonian's regents dated December 8, 1847, that the institution "organize a system of observation which shall extend as far as possible over the North American continent." The following year Henry initiated a volunteer weather observation program.

By 1860, the Smithsonian volunteer network encompassed more than 500 reporting stations. A series of devastating spring and summer tornadoes that year prompted Henry to request information from eye-witnesses. In 1862 the Smithsonian distributed circulars to the public warning of the dangers posed by tornadoes and asking for continued reports and data on these storms. The public's response was so great that in 1872 the institution issued a four-page pamphlet listing the questions observers should attempt to answer when reporting a tornado, including the date, location, length and width of path, direction of speed of movement, color of sky, and shape of funnel.

Accounts of intense storms might have occasionally appeared in the *Monthly Weather Review* or the *Monthly Weather Summary of States,* but meteorologists appeared to have reached a general consensus that forecasting tornadoes would do more harm than good. Continuing the precedent set by the Signal Corps, the Weather Bureau Stations Regulations of 1905 contained the statement, "Forecasts of tornadoes are prohibited." When conditions were favorable for tornado formation, district forecasters could use the term *severe thunderstorm* or *severe local storms,* but only the chief of the U.S. Weather Bureau, or, in his absence, the chief of the Forecast Service could use the phrase "conditions are favorable for destructive local storms." The restrictions remained in place until 1938.

A tornado can be seen in the swirling column of dust and debris under this supercell mesocyclone near Akron, Colorado, on June 14, 1990. Looking a bit like an alien spacecraft beaming up samples of earth, this huge storm spawned at least five tornadoes, as well as hail the size of baseballs. The rotating wall cloud and the updraft column (above the funnel) can be seen clearly. Photo: Eugene McCaul Jr.

During this period, citizens of tornado-prone areas learned to rely on their senses, observations of nature, and *The Farmer's Almanac* for weather predictions. Folk wisdom had taught Plains residents that the sky would often turn green, the wind would cease blowing, and animals would become agitated just before a tornado. One Apache method of weather forecasting was reading patterns in bear grease. According to this theory, animal cells respond to the weather even after the animal has died. The bear grease in animal bladders or jars formed various patterns on the sides of the containers, and reportedly tornadoes would follow observations of funnel shapes that appeared in the grease.

The U.S. Navy Department of Aeronautics issued a directive on tornadoes in March 1943. The report acknowledged that tornadoes were impossible to forecast because of their highly localized nature but that if naval station personnel had adequate warning of an approaching tornado, they could help pilots fly their aircraft to safety. In light of this directive, the navy's aerological officer at Hensley Field in Dallas, Texas, requested a network around the naval installations in the Dallas-Fort Worth area; the Weather Bureau complied in August 1943. The following spring, Civil Defense officials met with their counterparts from the U.S. Weather Bureau, the Army, and Navy to discuss Civil Defense's participation in the Severe Storm Warning Service. At the meeting, Weather Bureau personnel agreed to train and coordinate the observers that Civil Defense would provide, and the U.S. Army Air Corps and Navy advised the Weather Bureau where they needed networks. By February 1945, some 162 Severe Storm Warning Service networks with 3,685 observers were operating.

Methods of spreading the warning varied during the 1950s from company and fire department sirens to rail-yard whistles. Radio, however, was the most common method of disseminating tornado warnings. Broadcasting of weather reports over commercial radio stations began in the early 1920s. Only 20 of the nation's 36 commercial stations had a license to carry Weather Bureau forecasts by 1922, but the ultimate plan was for at least one station in each state to distribute official weather forecasts and warnings. The bureau certified all 140 existing stations for weather broadcasts in January 1923. Over the next few years the bureau and radio stations created links that enabled stations to cover local threats in a timely manner.

Most storm-spotter networks phoned radio stations in their areas to report tornadoes, and the radio stations relayed the warnings to their listening audiences. Over 95 percent of American households had radios by 1950. Only 5 percent of American households had a television in 1950, although both the number of sets and stations increased dramatically during the decade. This new medium, which would become the public's chief source of severe-storm warnings in the future, cautiously entered its new role in Oklahoma City in 1952, when the chief of the Weather Bureau granted WKY (now KTVY), the city's sole television station, permission to use Tinker Field's tornado predictions on the air. To avoid a panic, the WKY announcer would preface all warnings or weather information with the following statement: "We will pause a moment in our regular schedule in order to bring you some important weather information."

When a hook echo appeared on the Weather Bureau's radar screen in Wichita Falls, Texas, on April 3, 1964, station KAUZ's cameras began a live scan of the skies. As a spectacular twister roared through parts of the city, the station rewarded its viewers with the first live television broadcast of a tornado.

—*Marlene Bradford*

This enormous tornado was photographed in July 2002 from a single-engine plane during a cloud-seeding project. The tornado stayed in a rural area 15 miles northwest of Colby, Kansas, and damage was limited to a wrecked irrigation system and uprooted trees. Photo: Jason LaFontaine/Painet, Inc.

ROBERT FITZROY & THE SCIENCE OF WEATHER FORECASTING

LEFT: *Wild seas of the Drake Passage off the southernmost tip of South America. When Robert Fitzroy was in command of the HMS* Beagle, *he surveyed the coast of South America and produced charts so good that they were still in use during World War II. Photo: Galen Rowell/Mountain Light*

ABOVE: *Painting of Robert Fitzroy, inventor of the weather forecast. Photo: Courtesy of the British Crown, © 2007, the Met Office*

In 1836, Charles Darwin had been at sea for five years, traveling aboard HMS *Beagle* with a man who desperately wished his friendship. In fact, he had invited Darwin along as ship's naturalist precisely so that he could have someone to talk with, since the ordinary sailors of the British Navy could hardly be expected to keep up their end of a conversation. But Darwin and his benefactor had to struggle, too, to find things to talk about over those five long years, for Darwin, impatient and preoccupied, was well on his way to declaring his iconoclastic theory of evolution, while Robert Fitzroy, *Beagle*'s captain, was a religious fundamentalist who would sooner put the young scientist on an ice floe than admit that the Bible might be anything other than the literal truth.

That is how history remembers Fitzroy, if it remembers him at all. The image is quite unfair, and quite misleading. Darwin, a clergyman's son, was as religiously inclined as Fitzroy, while Fitzroy was well versed in science and expressed his own doubts whether earth had really been created, as the fundamentalists had it, in 4004 BC. Their positions solidified in opposite corners only long after they had returned to England. Then, in 1860, Fitzroy, by now an admiral in the Royal Navy and an ardent anti-evolutionist, turned up at a lecture given by Darwin at Oxford University and turned it into a grand debate—one that Fitzroy eventually lost.

Born in 1805, Fitzroy was well educated and interested in the world around him. He earned a perfect score on the exam that allowed him to graduate from naval college, and, when given his choice of assignments, he asked to join a survey of Tierra del Fuego, the little-known land at the southern tip of South America. There Fitzroy experienced, among other phenomena, the howling wind known locally as the *pampero*, which he would later describe in exacting scientific detail. His reports from Tierra del Fuego were so thorough and well written that he was called to the Admiralty before the Royal Navy's hydrographer, a man named Francis Beaufort.

Beaufort presented him with an assignment: Fitzroy was to return to South America on HMS *Beagle*, taking wind measurements along the coast, using a scale that Beaufort had devised—the Beaufort scale.

The *Beagle* was to be outfitted with a newfangled invention known as a lightning rod, as well as theodolites, barometers, and chronometers, all to keep an eye on the weather. When he was finished with South America, Beaufort instructed, Fitzroy was to do the same sort of surveying in the South Pacific, along the African coast, and indeed anywhere that English sailors might venture—and to take his time about it.

Thus began the five-year voyage that Charles Darwin made famous. On this and other scientific journeys, Fitzroy carried out his duties in exemplary fashion, so much so that in 1854 he was appointed to head a new department of the government's Board of Trade: an office devoted to meteorological statistics and research. Fitzroy immediately set about placing weather-observing equipment on ships in every port in England, eventually recruiting some 80 captains to make standardized measurements of the weather wherever their voyages took them. While he waited for the first reports to come in, he devised a new method of recording weather data, which he called "wind stars," showing wind directions and intensities around the world. Ships' navigators came to swear by his careful charts, which saved countless lives as they warned sailors of rough passages.

Fitzroy went on to invent a barometer now called the Fitzroy storm glass, still an accurate means of foretelling heavy weather. Of more lasting importance, he wedded meteorological science to advances in communications technology, devising the first scientific weather forecast. His method used the telegraph to transmit data from far-flung weather stations, which in itself was not an original idea; Fitzroy's contribution came in plotting that data in relation to the prevailing wind, demonstrating that strong weather systems generally moved over the British Isles from the west and moved at a pace that could be calculated. Thus a storm bursting over Galway Bay at Sunday breakfast, say, could be predicted within a reasonable margin of error to arrive in London by tea time. Once again, the ability to warn ships of impending storms and their approximate time of arrival saved many lives.

Fitzroy gathered the fruits of his long years of observation and experimentation in *The Weather Book*, published in 1862, in which he coined the phrase "an ocean of air." Almanac writers used his charts to devise weather forecasts that were as accurate as could be, given the time and technology; soon the *Times* of London would publish weather forecasts daily, even if its editors were in the habit of blaming Fitzroy personally when the forecasts were off.

Recognized as one of the great pioneers in scientific meteorology today, Robert Fitzroy received little praise for his work in his own time. Melancholic, in poor health, and on the losing side of the Darwinian debate, he took his own life on April 30, 1865, at the age of 59. He was forgotten for years, but then happily rediscovered. Today the British government's Meteorological Office and National Meteorological Library and Archive are located on Fitzroy Road in Exeter, England, and modern atmospheric scientists proudly acknowledge him as the founder of their discipline.

—*Gregory McNamee*

The Coast Guard Cutter Tamaroa's *rigid hull inflatable rescue boat is sent to help the sailing vessel* Satori, *which needed help about 75 miles south of Nantucket Island after being caught in a northeaster-like storm that raked New England on Halloween week. Photo: Weatherstock*

READING BETWEEN THE LINES

LEFT and ABOVE: *This bristlecone pine lies alone on the side of a hill high in the White Mountains of California. It is a fine example of krummholz—a term mountain geographers use for trees formed by the wind (the German translation for krummholz is "bent wood"). Locked within the ancient bristlecones' rings are records of past regional droughts and temperature swings. Photos: Ed Darack*

It twists upward from the rocky face of Ontario's Niagara escarpment, more bare trunk than tree now, and yet each spring, leaves still flourish from its few still-living branches. The process is remarkable, since this ancient northern white cedar (*Thuja occidentalis*) first sprouted from the cliff in AD 998. During the intervening ten centuries, this aging tree has recorded every rainfall, blizzard, drought, and wildfire that swept this region—a priceless meteorological record. It's all in the tree rings.

The same kind of weather data is exposed in the cut ends of the branches you prune from that tree in your yard, or in the stump of a Christmas tree. The grain in wood is simply these annual rings, cut obliquely; the figured wood of an old cabinet or desk really shows us swirling patterns of weather past.

Dendroclimatologists are the experts who can tell us this weather. Repositories such as the International Tree-Ring Data Bank are the official "library" for their findings, maintaining data collected by thousands of experts who have studied virtually every species of tree across the planet. It is, in effect, a forest of knowledge. And in every sample, variations in the tree's grain preserve a history of weather, often in startling detail.

For example, the closely spaced rings in a Rocky Mountain juniper (*Juniperus scopulorum*) recall a long-ago dry spell. The dark inclusions partly obliterate the lines. These are burn scars. This forest so wanted for rain that it caught fire. Based on the annual rings (each ring is composed of early and late season growth), we can pinpoint the blaze to July or August 1779. Many dendrological samples are centuries old, the last living witnesses to past events. Think of a tree as a kind of weather chart recorder that records very slowly.

The basic theory sounds simple: wide rings in a tree indicate wet seasons, narrower ones mark the dry years. Yet the complexities of a forest (each tree lives in its own microenvironment, and even woodpeckers can change how a tree grows) make turning tree rings back into weather more like trying to glue autumn leaves back on the trees where they fell. Raw measurements of rings must be taken from many trees in an area, then reduced to graphs, called skeleton plots. Measurements can be taken from living trees (which are cored using tiny probes, to avoid damaging them), as well as from dead trees, which stopped recording weather long ago.

Then similar, repeating patterns among these samples are correlated in order to "synchronize" the trees. This is how years are assigned to rings. It's something like breaking an enemy code using many tiny messages. The advantage lies in stringing the histories of different trees together, producing a plot of weather spanning much longer than the oldest living trees. These are called chronologies. It is all the brainchild of A. E. Douglass, an astronomer who developed the theory that tree rings were records of solar cycles of growth. He eventually determined that by studying the rings, one could reclaim some of earth's oldest climate records.

The stories the trees can tell sometimes rewrite our history. In rings corresponding to the year 1588, from a stand of bald cypress (*Taxodium distichum*) in Virginia's tidewater region, David Stahle of the University of Arkansas Tree Ring Lab has discovered evidence of the worst drought to strike the Americas during the past eight centuries. With this finding, the disappearance of the fabled "lost colony of Roanoke" may finally be solved, for the doomed colonists vanished from that spot in that very year.

Far more ancient timbers, preserved where they fell, can reconstruct weather from the prehistoric past. Stahle is currently exploring the remains of a 50,000-year-old forest, buried beneath modern Maryland. Once chronicled, the rain and heat that drove Pleistocene herds across ancient America will be charted nearly as accurately as last month's average rainfalls. How these results may transform our familiar "museum" images of the Ice Age and early humankind, only time and the trees can tell.

Still other findings prove as current as the nightly news. Each spring, wildfires are reported raging across the western states. Naturally, we blame the droughts. But is the weather changing, or have we changed the forests by logging too much old growth, leaving the forest less able to bear these fires naturally? At the University of Arizona Laboratory of Tree-Ring Research, Paul R. Sheppard and his team are exploring the relationship between rainfall and fire records in old Western forests to understand fire and weather in the preindustrial age better. If fire has changed but weather has not, we may need to reexamine our forest management policies.

Like discovering an old diary stuffed in the rafters, an old house or barn inadvertently preserves a record of the weather. It's stored in the grain of the beams and siding that make up the structure. At the Laboratory for Tree Ring Science at the University of Tennessee, Henri D. Grissino-Mayer has analyzed timbers from an aging frontier dwelling, long purported to be the log cabin where Abraham Lincoln was born. Is the verdict in the rings? The 16th president may have been "honest" Abe, but this cabin wasn't. Its timbers were felled in the 1840s; Lincoln was born in 1809. Perhaps this later cabin contains an occasional authentic log—making it, in Lincoln's own words, "a house divided against itself." It would seem that the history of weather, as stored in the trees, still has much to tell us about our past, including an occasional breath of fresh air.

—*Nick D'Alto*

Ponderosa pines rise into the Sierra sky near Sonora Pass, California. Photo: Ed Darack

46

THE INVENTION OF DENDROCHRONOLOGY

By training, Andrew Ellicott Douglass (1867–1962) was an astronomer. In 1894 he was hired by Percival Lowell to select a location and to oversee the construction of a new observatory—the great Lowell Observatory in Flagstaff, Arizona. There Douglass spent seven years assisting in the discovery of distant stars and planets, until an unfortunate dispute with Lowell led to his dismissal.

Resourceful and well rounded, Douglass made ends meet by teaching Spanish and geography at what is now Northern Arizona University while serving as a probate judge in Flagstaff. Looking for some way to connect the record of sunspot cycles to climate, it was among the tall ponderosa pines of campus and city where he developed the theory that tree rings were records of solar cycles of growth: the wide rings of certain species of trees recorded wet years, narrow rings dry years. Douglass found that he was able to correlate tree ring patterns with the time of various historical events, both natural and anthropogenic. In all events, each year a tree adds a new layer of wood, a ring that can be counted. From this observation, Douglass conjectured that by studying the climatological record of a region such as the Colorado Plateau, predictions could be made about future weather cycles.

Douglass moved south to Tucson in 1906 to teach at the University of Arizona. There he elaborated the science of "dendrochronology: which uses tree rings to determine the age of a particular piece of wood." He developed a ponderosa tree ring chronology dating back hundreds of years, which enabled archaeologists to use timber taken from sites such as Mesa Verde to date their construction—an important window on prehistory.

Tree ring analysis can also be used to diagnose the effects of air and water pollution and to adjust irrigation cycles in arid-lands farming. At present, the chronology—established mostly from ponderosa and bristlecone pines—has been extended to 7000 BC, and efforts are being made to push that date back even further, to the ending of the last Ice Age.

—Nick D'Alto

PREDICTING WAVES

In the last decade, both the science and the art of surf forecasting have become incredibly precise for surf spots from up and down the coast of Malibu in California to Cape Hatteras on the East Coast to Hawaii's pipeline and spots in Australia, Fiji, South Africa, and Europe. Culling data from automated buoy reports, ship reports, wind information from satellites, and the bathymetry of specific surf spots, forecasters have created computer models that can predict the tide and quality of waves days and weeks ahead of time. Tens of thousands of surfers throughout the United States are plugged into Internet swell forecasts that have made finding the perfect wave as simple as typing on your computer.

"We're getting to the point that we are now able to predict to the hour when a large swell is going to hit," says Sean Collins, a veteran Huntington Beach forecaster and corporate officer with Surfline (www.surfline.com), an online weather and wave forecasting business. The company has eight forecasters on duty with the sole job of predicting waves. In the late 1970s, Collins got an underground reputation among surfers for his uncanny "spot-on" predictions of southern swells on California beaches generated by storms off the coast of New Zealand and Antarctica. Because the waves are generated thousands of miles away, it is often difficult to pinpoint where they will hit. Exact measurements of the strength and duration of those storms is vital. Underestimating the actual wind speed in a storm brewing at sea by just five miles per hour could result in a significant error in estimating the strength of waves.

Waves are a visible display of the energy in bodies of water. In the ocean, waves represent about one-third of all the energy available, with the other two-thirds linked to currents. Scientists are still investigating the many forces that cause and influence waves. Wind is responsible for most typical waves, first creating small ripples on the surface of the water, minor variations that are small enough to be flattened by surface tension unless they can grow in size. Their growth varies, depending on the temperature and salinity of the water. Ripples are usually not considered waves until the wavelength—the distance from crest to crest—is at least four inches, about the width of the average person's hand.

Crashing coastal waves like these at Pt. Pinos, Asilomar State Beach,
California, are becoming easier to predict for veteran forecasters.
Photo: Rich Reid

CLASSES OF WAVES

Type 1
Surface Waves include all normal surface movement caused by the wind, including ripples, swells, and waves.

Type 2
Internal Waves are created by the movement of subsurface currents over irregularities on the sea floor.

Type 3
Seismic Waves can be triggered by earthquakes or underwater landslides (also called "tsunamis").

Type 4
Solitary Waves are usually stable, single waves resulting from some human activity or from a tidal surge moving over an underground obstacle.

Type 5
Tide Waves are affected by the cycles of the moon and the sun.

Type 6
Planetary Waves are influenced by the effect of the earth's spin on ocean currents

Once a wave begins to form, its potential height is determined by three factors: the speed of the wind, the distance the wind can blow across the surface of the water without interference, and the length of time the wind blows without changing either direction or velocity. The ultimate size of a wave is limited by the very force of the wind that creates it; the tops of waves that become too steep are blown over, hence the term "whitecaps." Some waves eventually turn into swells, the correct term for waves that have moved outside the area where they were generated. Waves actively being produced by the wind vary considerably in size and shape, but as they settle into swells, the size and shape become more uniform. Even without the continual presence of wind, waves and swells gradually lose energy because of the drag created by the turbulence of the water in which they move, a process known as "wave dispersion." But large swells—those created by big storms—can travel long distances, literally from one end of the earth to the other, without fading away.

Collins's company has pioneered predicting monstrous surf, waves in excess of 40 or 50 feet high and as tall as 100 feet. When the waves are that big, surfers cannot even paddle into them and they must rely on Jet Skis to tow them into the fast moving walls of water. Finding storms that generate swells of that size is not difficult, but finding places where the waves will break undisturbed by the weather is another matter. As Collins states, only a handful of spots around the world can hold large surf. Five years ago, a reef 100 miles offshore from southern California was ridden for the first time because of the surf and weather forecasts made by Sean Collins and his team. "That was something I'm very proud of," he said.

—*Scott Hadly*

LIGHT

LIGHTNING, RAINBOWS, AURORAS, COMETS, AND RAYS

"Daddy, why is the sky red?" might query a young descendent of Earth residing in a future Martian colony. And why blue here on Earth, except when it's orange, red, pink, or gray? For those taking the time to look skyward, a decided minority in our frantic, increasingly urbanized society, the celestial dome displays a never-ending kaleidoscope of tints, hues and textures, all in High Definition, without monthly cable or satellite charges.

The light detected by our eyes is just a fraction of the electromagnetic radiation spectrum emitted by our nearest star. Visible light is absorbed, scattered, reflected, and refracted by molecules, water droplets, ice crystals, and atmospheric layers, which extract the spectrum's rainbow colors. Shorter than violet, UV wavelengths can burn our skin while those longer than red can be felt radiating from a brick wall releasing the heat from a day's intense sunshine. Highly energetic particles streaming from the solar nuclear furnace energize the upper atmosphere into multi-hued curtains draped around both poles, not only on the third rock from the sun, but on Jupiter and Saturn as well.

Once thought a harbinger of war, the aurora sky show gets two thumbs up from all critics, and is also a reminder there is indeed "weather" in near space. Cosmic radiation and magnetic disturbances can cripple satellites, expose astronauts and transpolar airline passengers to worrisome radiation dosages, and trigger massive power outages in the intertwined electrical grids on the planet below. The same solar wind which bombards our upper atmosphere vectors the glowing tails of comets like Hale-Bopp to always point away from the sun which they orbit.

LEFT: *The vertical streak of reddish light seen here in Norman, Oklahoma, is called a sun pillar. This relatively rare phenomenon is caused from reflected light on the tops and bottoms of vertically aligned, falling ice crystals. Photo: Charles A. Doswell III*

FOLLOWING PAGES: *A midsummer storm coming south up the valley to the Yampa Valley in northwest Colorado creates a magnificent rainbow over the hayfields. The Yampa Valley and surrounding area contain several geothermal hot springs. Photo: Rod Hanna*

Once an omen of pestilence, Comet Halley's return as predicted by Sir Edmond is now celebrated; we, meanwhile, send probes to sample icy, rocky cometary surfaces and worry if after 65 million years, another really, really big one might impact us. Everyone's favorite, the rainbow, once sent a Franciscan monk to prison for life. Around 1265, Roger Bacon displeased the ecclesiastical authorities by daring to demonstrate how raindrops refracted sunlight to decorate the heavens without need of direct Divine intervention.

Yet one light in the sky, brighter and hotter than the sun, should be feared, or at least respected. We now know neither Thor nor Jupiter nor Zeus hurl the lightning flashes which strike the U.S. 30 million times yearly, killing perhaps a hundred Americans and thousands worldwide, with damage mounting into the billions. Following the 30:30 rule can save you. If the time delay between the brilliant flash and the resounding boom of the thunder is less than 30 seconds, the next bolt could well strike where you are standing. Seek safety inside a well-constructed building and avoid conducting objects with pathways to the outside. Stay inside until 30 minutes after the last rumble of thunder. Many fatalities occur as people venture outside to admire the receding storm, only to encounter one of the many strikes occurring outside the storm's rain footprint.

Perhaps that thunderstorm was triggered by a sea breeze on a tropical coastline, where evening finds you relaxing on the beach as the sun sets slowly into the ocean, allowing a glimpse of the elusive green flash. This brief emerald apparition results from sunlight's passage through layers of moisture and temperature near the sea surface. Or maybe it is just Mother Nature giving you a knowing wink because you took time to slow down, smell any available roses, and especially watch the never ending light show that is our sky.

—*Walter Lyons, CCM*

BASIC LIGHTNING SAFETY TIPS
Recommended by the National Weather Service:

1. Seek shelter immediately if a thunderstorm (or storm clouds) threatens. Golf courses, playing fields, hiking trails or any open area are especially dangerous.

2. If caught in the open, avoid tall, isolated trees. Crouch down and keep a low profile. Groups of people should keep apart. Avoid hilltops.

3. Get out of water and off small boats.

4. Avoid metal objects such as golf clubs, tractors, fences, metal pipes, tools and clotheslines.

5. Stay away from open doors, windows, radiators, bathtubs/showers, and sinks. Do not use plug-in electrical appliances.

6. Avoid using the telephone, except for emergencies. Lightning can travel through phone lines.

7. If you feel your hair stand on end or your skin tingle, lightning may be about to strike. Crouch down and cover your head. Do not lie flat.

8. Learn CPR. Many people who have been hit by lightning can be revived by basic CPR. People who are hit by lightning do not carry an electrical charge.

LEFT: *A tropical storm that had pounded Baja, California, drifted north toward California's Central Valley, igniting this rare lightning storm over San Francisco on September 8, 1999. Long-time residents claim that it was the largest display of lightning they had ever seen. Photo: Douglas Keister*

RIGHT: *Just like a vintage movie, this image captures the romance of the landscape that lured settlers west. Shot in Arizona northwest of Tucson, this image captures a spectacular July lightning storm looking west toward the sunset and the Tucson Mountains. Photo: Keith Kent/Peter Arnold, Inc.*

EARTH'S MAGNETIC LIGHTS

The aurora borealis, or the northern lights, is among nature's most awe-inspiring sights. Equally impressive is the aurora australis, or the southern lights, visible in the Southern Hemisphere. Both are earthly phenomena, occurring high in the atmosphere, but are spawned some 93 million miles away in the sun.

Energetic electrically charged particles (mostly electrons, protons, and alpha particles, or helium nuclei) continuously speed outward from the sun at about a million miles per hour. This is called the solar wind. When there is particularly strong activity on the sun, typically corresponding to the sun's 11-year sunspot cycle, the solar wind will be particularly strong.

Since they are electrically charged, the particles (mostly energetic protons) that cause the auroras are attracted to earth's north and south magnetic poles. That is why the auroras are more frequently seen the closer you are to the poles. As these energetic particles spiral down along the magnetic lines of force, they interact with atoms and molecules in the upper atmosphere (mostly oxygen and nitrogen), causing them to glow or fluoresce.

Untold numbers of these fluorescing particles cause the aurora, which may appear as anything from a faint red glow to an elaborate fluttering curtain or flower-like pattern.

Each type of display can be classified into one of four phases. Phase 1 is a featureless glow. Phase 2 is a well-defined arc of light. Phase 3 is a moving curtain of light, possibly with streamers or rays that fade in and out. Phase 4 is a stage of irregularity in which the display appears broken, patchy, and flaming. Phase 3, the most spectacular and best to photograph, happens more often during years of peak sunspots. This phase can dramatically illuminate the entire sky and landscape manyfold in less than a minute, and to various degrees with colors. Unfortunately, this phase typically is the shortest in duration most of the time. Recently discovered large-scale winds at great altitude may be responsible in part for the various auroral forms.

The northern lights come in many colors, although greenish-white is the most common, followed by yellow and rarer red during intense surges.

Photographs show the colors more vividly than they actually appear, but they still cannot come near to showing the graceful motions of the auroral curtain and that of its details. These and the awesome spiraling and converging of the dynamic auroral plasma into a wondrous beautiful corona overhead are sights that not even Scheherazade of *Arabian Nights' Entertainment* could imagine.

—*Jay Brausch*

A brilliant pallet of "aurora" colors light up the sky above the Talkeetna Mountains near Broad Pass, Alaska, in the early morning hours. The aurora borealis (called the aurora australis in the Southern Hemisphere) is a geomagnetic storm of electrically charged particles from the sun spiraling toward earth's magnetic north and south poles. A reaction between these earth-bound particles and earth's upper atmosphere causes them to fluoresce—to emit electromagnetic radiation, which is seen as visible light. Photo: Fred Hirschmann

PHASE 1

PHASE 2

The aurora has four basic phases of behavior, which can come in any order in a given display. No display is exactly like another, and a display doesn't have to go through all four phases in a night. They are the glow (phase 1), the homogenous arc (phase 2), the rayed arc (phase 3), and the "chaotic" patches (phase 4). Often, a display will appear to have a combination of phases, but for the sake of simplicity, the phase that is most dominant is what is recorded.

Phases 3 and 4 are the active phases, and phases 1 and 2 are the quiescent (pre-surge) phases of behavior. The consistent recording and measure of the frequency of visible auroras from a given location over the long-term is also a measure of solar activity. The hyperactive sun by means of presenting unusually high amounts of auroras here is the greater indicator of the global warming phenomenon. Photos: Jay Brausch

LEFT: *In 1991, the Hekla volcano in Iceland erupted, sending ash to a height of 37,730 feet to meet auroras that were visible only about 62 miles overhead. The electrical discharges are visible in the night sky in a pattern that is roughly semicircular around the pole, and are often accompanied by strong geomagnetic disturbances. The occurrence of auroras follows a cycle similar to the sunspot cycle. Great auroral displays in mid-latitudes are usually associated with intense flares in the vicinity of sunspots. Photo: Sigurdur Stefnisson*

ABOVE: *Alaskan northern lights light up the sky and put on a beautiful display of color. Photos: Fred Hirschmann*

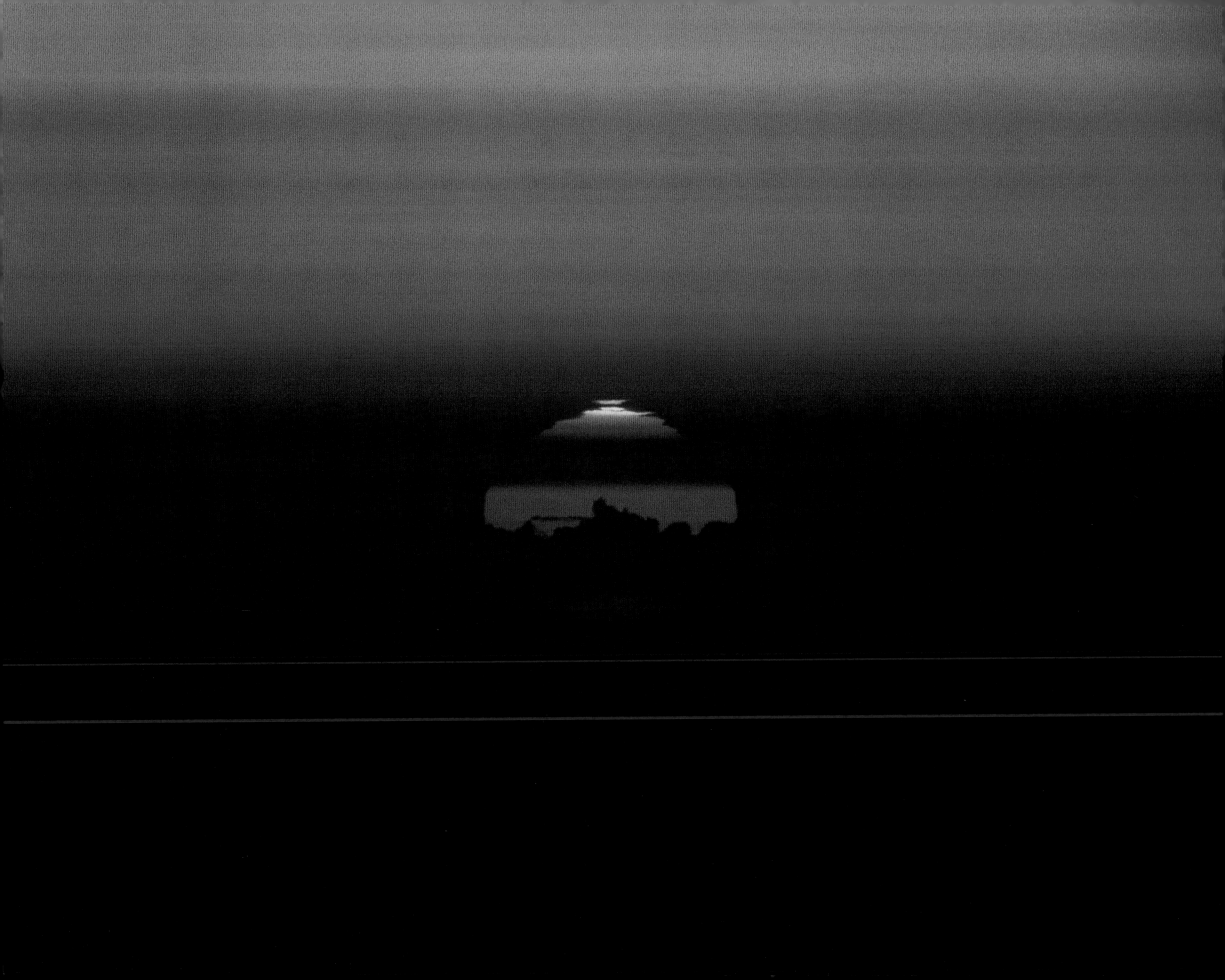

CAN YOU CATCH THE "GREEN FLASH"?

Have you ever seen a green star? Chances are, you haven't. But the light from all normal stars, including our sun, contains green light. In fact, most stars emit most colors of light. In the case of our sun, and stars like it, the combination of different wavelengths results in white or yellowish-white light.

But what about that green light? How do we know the sun has green light? Everyone has seen a rainbow with its arc of spectral colors—red, orange, yellow, green, blue, indigo, and violet. So when sunlight is bent by millions of rain droplets, through a combination of refraction and reflection, it is broken down into different colors, including green.

There is another way to see the sun's elusive green light, by observing a transient if not rare phenomenon called the "Green Flash." It sounds like a comic book superhero, and for most people it is just about as real. But this and other phenomena are real. Under the right conditions, the Green Flash may be visible at the top of the setting sun, seconds after the body of the sun has slipped below the visible horizon. (It is sometimes visible with the rising sun, too, but those observations are more difficult.)

When a rainbow breaks down light into its constituent colors, it does so with water droplets, which act as tiny prisms. But the earth's atmosphere itself can bend light, sometimes causing us to see different colors at different times. Look at a very bright star near the horizon on a warm, humid night. Chances are you will see that star flicker and change color very rapidly. The effect of the starlight passing through many different cells of atmosphere at slightly different temperatures and pressures causes different colors of light to be bent differently. In one split second the red colors may be bent in our direction, while in the next split second it may be the blue light. When the sun is near the horizon, its light is passing through thicker layers of atmosphere than when it is high overhead. Thus the effect of the air in bending sunlight is greatest at this time. So the sun's light can be dispersed into different colors. At this time you may also notice the sun appears flattened, which is another effect of the atmosphere.

PRECEDING PAGES 82–83: *A polar bear enjoys a stroll on a frigid November evening in Manitoba, Canada, as the illusion of three suns lights his way. This atmospheric phenomenon, called a "sun dog," occurs when ice crystals in the air bend sunlight at a 22 degree angle, not unlike a prism, and appear prominently when the sun is low in the sky. Photo: Steve Bloom*

LEFT: *This is the Green Segment which differs from the elusive Green Flash only in that the disk of the sun is still visible. In this striking image, shot from Mauna Kea Volcano, the sculpted shadows across the bottom of the sun are distant clouds over the Pacific. Photo: Kenneth D. Langford*

Why don't we see the sun change into all these different colors at sunset? The blue wavelengths are scattered by molecules of air. Because their wavelengths are comparable to the size of air molecules, they have a more difficult time finding a straight line. Instead, they are bounced off into all directions, which is why the sky is blue. On the other hand, orange and yellow light is not scattered but absorbed by the atmosphere (primarily by water vapor, oxygen, and ozone). So the setting sun typically doesn't appear orange or yellow, because the atmosphere absorbs those wavelengths.

The red light usually passes through, which is why the setting sun frequently appears red. But like red light, green light is neither absorbed nor dispersed. And when the red light is fading, for just a brief moment, the top of the sun may appear greenish. Sometimes this green edge of the sun appears to detach itself and float above the sun for a few moments. This is the "Green Flash." Although the Green Flash has been known for a long time, relatively few people have seen it because it requires a certain set of circumstances and is very fleeting. Few people are looking at the right time.

Can you see the Green Flash? Although the Green Flash is best seen through a telescope or binoculars, we emphatically do not advise this. It is never safe to look directly at the sun, either with just the eye or with optical aid. In the last few moments before setting, the sun's light is usually greatly attenuated, but anyone who looks at it must do so at his or her own risk.

The Green Flash and other color phenomena are best seen when there is a low, clear horizon without clouds, dust, haze, or any form of pollution. From a mountaintop or over the ocean are typically cited as the best observing conditions. The flash is a fleeting and somewhat capricious phenomenon, which some observers have tried for decades to see and have never succeeded.

—*Larry Sessions*

ABOVE: *Here the "Blue Flash" is seen over the Atlantic Ocean from Southampton, Bermuda. The blue color, perhaps with a hint of violet, is more likely to be seen when the air is haze and pollution-free. Photo: Kenneth D. Langford*

FOLLOWING PAGES 88–89: *This spectacular summer storm lit up the Great Sand Dunes of southern Colorado for some time, accompanied by noisy thunder but very little rain. Photo: E. R. Degginger*

HALE-BOPP: COMET OF THE CENTURY?

In 1997, Hale-Bopp graced the dawn sky of late February and early March with its gas tail and a breathtaking increase in brightness. Then, in mid-March, the comet crossed to the evening sky where millions more people saw it plainly with the unaided eye. Hale-Bopp posed magnificently with the moon in early April and remained visible without optical aid until early May.

Schoolteachers described Hale-Bopp as the only thing they'd ever witnessed that got kids away from TV sets for a while. Hale-Bopp was the only modern comet bright enough to reach for many weeks into even the most light-polluted cities—a torch of hope from the world of Nature and grand perspectives.

Hale-Bopp's head—a cloud of glowing gas twice the sun's width in space—was one of the largest ever recorded. The head featured vast perfect "hoods" of golden sunlit dust that were visible even in fairly small telescopes for about two months. These were being puffed out by the icy nucleus of the comet. The nucleus produced about 100 times as much gas as Halley's Comet does at comparable distances from the sun and probably many more times as much dust.

Despite its tremendous true length, Hale-Bopp's tail appeared foreshortened by pointing mostly away from us. And the better scattering angles for the dust tails of Comet Bennett in 1970 and Comet West in 1976 helped make those tails bright for a greater apparent length than Hale-Bopp's. But in Hale-Bopp the brilliant section of tail was at least long enough and certainly bright enough to be plainly visible from big cities and to identify the object immediately as a comet.

Hale-Bopp never came close to earth or the sun. But its intrinsic brightness was rivaled by only a few others in the past 400 or 500 years. And Hale-Bopp was a "great comet"—a comet brighter than the Big Dipper stars when out of twilight in full darkness—for longer than any comet on record.

—*Fred Schaaf*

LEFT: *The grandeur of the comet Hale-Bopp over the mountains. Photo: Paul Neiman*

WIND

TORNADOES, DUST STORMS, WATERSPOUTS, AND HURRICANES

The names of earth's winds are legion: cyclone, twister, tornado, willy willy, dust devil, waterspout, katabatic, blue norther, Santa Ana, foehn, sirocco, haboob, Tehuantepecer, chubasco, brubu, kona, laventer, bora, mistral, blad, williwaw, and even brickfielder. That last name given by the early residents of Sydney, Australia, for the gusty blows from the south bringing red, dust-filled air from the brick kilns outside of town.

Farmers, sailors, fisherpersons, or whoever spends time in the outdoors, learn their local winds well, with new zephyrs denominated with every change of geography. But all wind is basically the same: the movement of that fluid we call air from one place to another. Scientists can even quantify it mathematically rather easily on paper. Start with a pressure gradient force, take into account the Coriolis effect from our spinning planet, subtract the drag of friction and turbulence, and round it off by accounting for the centripetal and centrifugal forces of spinning vortices.

LEFT: *This classic F2 twister near Watonga, Oklahoma, is shown here at the beginning of its "roping" stage. The funnel was on the ground for 20 minutes, and was only 1 of 26 tornadoes in Oklahoma on that day. Photo: Hank Baker*

FOLLOWING PAGE: *A Kansas state trooper quickly throws his patrol car into reverse to avoid being sent to the Land of Oz by this menacing twister near Pretty Prairie, Kansas, on April 11, 2002. The tornado, which passed within 900 yards of the officer, had been on the ground for nearly 30 minutes when it suddenly changed directions. Photo: Jim Reed/Getty Images*

FOLLOWING PAGE 95: *This tornado was the first of 10 to touch down on May 29, 2004. It developed four miles east of Attica, Kansas, and moved north through rural farm country, lasting 24 minutes. The bottom half of the tornado was illuminated by the setting sun, creating a beautiful orange glow. The outbreak was caused by a lone supercell moving eastward. This tornado had an F1 rating with associated wind speeds of 80 to 110 miles per hour. Photo: Eric Nguyen*

Simple in theory, perhaps, yet the complexity of real-world air motion requires more than a little scientific ingenuity to measure and record the winds' every gust and ebb on all their myriad scales. We find the wind in thunderstorm updrafts suspending a giant hailstone, tortuously swirling around a home as a thunderstorm gust front tears across a suburb, advancing as a great army of air across continents with seasonal monsoons, roaring along as a jet-stream river girdling the globe, and as the gentle upliftings and subsidings of the general circulation which define where moisture-laden storms rampage or where clear, hot air endlessly sinks over barren deserts. Some winds of the tropics have personal names that will long be remembered by their victims: Mitch, Katrina, Iniki, and Tip. The thousand-plus tornadoes that annually assault our nation remain nameless, but their victims never forget the instant their lives were changed by the shrieking wind. By way of respite, dust devils and waterspouts seem almost playful, skittering above the scrub landscape of hot desert sands or the warm ocean.

Air may seem so tenuous, yet earth's winds do the heavy lifting of our climate system. Without the winds, the tropical regions would become unbearably hot and the poles numbingly cold. Winds carry moisture, making agriculture and civilization possible. Delay or failure of the Indian monsoon means drought and famine. Pacific winds create the coastal forests and snow packs of the American West. Sometimes winds hurling moisture against mountain barriers unleash torrential downpours, killer flash floods, and landslides.

The wind's potential to rip apart humanity's proud achievements increases with the square of its velocity as roofs are scattered across a neighborhood. Other less provocative winds transport great clouds of dust from central Asia, yellowing the western American skies each spring. The carbon black smoke of the Kuwaiti oil fires circumnavigated the world not once, but twice. Six inches of Georgia's topsoil are reputed to have blown in from the deserts of Africa.

Were it not for the semi-permanent bands such as the trade winds, ancient commerce and global exploration may have been constrained to landlocked migrations. Our world, our livelihoods, our everyday lives are perpetually influenced by the ceaseless wind—even during the calm before the storm.

—*Walter Lyons, CCM*

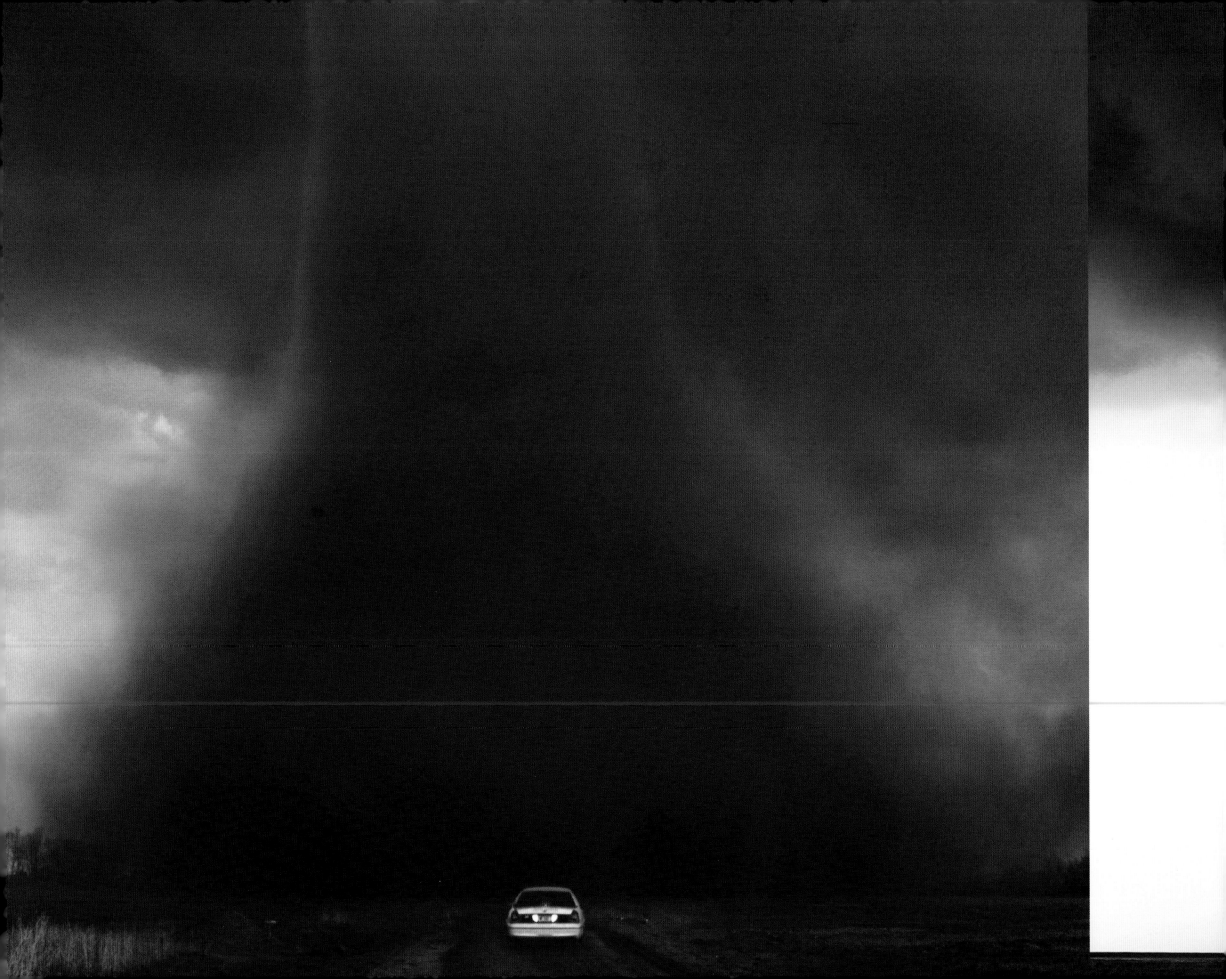

STORM DAMAGE

Mother Nature packs a wallop. The floods, wind, and hail that represent nature at its extreme are powerful forces that pose a serious threat to flora and fauna, the landscape, humans, and the structures in which they live and work. Modern technology provides significant protection against even the most extreme storms, but every year in the United States, storms still wreak havoc, producing billions of dollars of damage.

Hurricanes often get the most attention as devastating forces, but compared to thunderstorms, they are few and far between. The U.S. National Weather Service estimates that at any given time, about 2,000 thunderstorms take place throughout the world, but only severe thunderstorms are likely to cause serious damage. In the United States, about 10 percent of all thunderstorms are rated at this level, with winds of 58 miles per hour or more and/or with hail at least ¾ inch in diameter.

Tornadoes that accompany thunderstorms are well known for their dangerous wind, but more common are straight-line winds and microbursts, which can reach velocities of 100 miles per hour or more. About 40 percent of all property damage during thunderstorms is caused by this kind of wind, and annual losses from non-tornado winds are estimated to be about $200 million a year. By comparison, annual tornado damage is about $500 million a year. Most of the damage produced by wind occurs to the roofs and siding of buildings. A single shingle, lifted at its lower edge by wind gusts, exposes the underside of the overlying shingle; if the wind tears away the first, it creates a cascading chain of failure that can pull away dozens to hundreds more. With the strongest blows, the underlying sheathing or even the entire roof may be ripped away.

Despite the threat from wind, the greatest danger from thunderstorms is hail. Hail comes in various sizes, from pea-sized on up, and varies in density (number of hits per area) as well as impact speed (a factor related to how hard the wind is blowing the ice pellets when they hit). Although deaths from hail strikes are rare, damage to crops and structures is common. Annual crop losses in the United States alone are estimated to be at least $1 billion; non-crop damage averages about $350 million a year.

Most structural hail damage is to roofs. The major variables involved are the type of roofing material—asphalt shingles are the most vulnerable—and the angle of the roof. In general, the steeper the pitch, the

97

The record-tying nature of this tornado meant little to residents of Manchester, South Dakota, as their hometown disintegrated under the onslaught of this half-mile wide F4 tornado on June 24, 2003. Manchester, standing on the prairies since the 1880s, would never be rebuilt. Photo: Karen Leszke & Gene Rhoden

less the damage because falling hail produces less damage when hitting at an angle. These ice pellets create damage by knocking off the shingle's protective outer layer (usually a mineral coating), breaking off the edges, or penetrating completely through the material. In general, the warmer the temperature, the better asphalt shingles absorb hail impact without damage because they are more flexible when warm. Flexibility is also related to age: the older the shingles, the more likely they are dried out and brittle, increasing the potential for damage.

Crop damage from hail is linked not only to the size, density, and velocity of hail, but to the type of crop and the stage of plant growth. For a month or so after sprouting, for example, corn plants typically do not suffer much during a hailstorm because the plants are small and represent less of a target. From mid-summer on, however, it's a different story. Even a moderate hailstorm can ruin a corn crop because these plants do not recover when defoliated by falling ice. Soybeans, on the other hand, are better able to survive defoliation, at least early in a season. In order to assess the damage from hail, insurance agents who specialize in crop damage must use careful analysis that is specific to the crop that has been hit.

With or without tornadoes, a single severe thunderstorm can produce a tremendous trail of damage, and when multiple thunderstorms occur as outbreaks, the effects quickly amplify. The record for a single thunderstorm comes from a supercell on May 5, 1995, in the Dallas-Ft. Worth, Texas, area, with $1.1 to $2 billion in claims from a combination of wind, hail, and flooding.

Wind and hailstorms can spread destruction over many acres, accounting for their ability to rack up large losses. But lightning, although singular and narrowly focused, poses a more frequent threat. The most frequent range of loss is between $5,000 and $50,000 per strike (at least for those reported as causing damage); between 1959 and 1994, the National Weather Service lists 19,814 total damage-causing strikes. Most strikes hit only a single structure and cause limited damage per strike, especially if the structure is a residence. But up to 30 percent of all church fires are caused by lightning strikes, as are more than three-quarters of all accidents involving gas and oil storage tanks. When a single lightning strike produces the most expensive damage, it is usually because it triggers a wildfire. In the western United States alone, an estimated 10,000 such fires occur annually, with losses and suppression costs topping $100 million. In a strange example of natural cause and effect, the smoke and heat from large forest fires generate atmospheric conditions that produce even more lightning strikes, which cause even more wildfires.

For those suburban dwellers who think their sprawling communities represent more security than isolated houses in the country, there is bad news. According to some scientists, the increasing amount of urban structures clustered together often function as heat islands, and in some areas—Atlanta, Georgia, in particular—the added heat triggers a greater number of local thunderstorms. With these storms come more lightning strikes, and both the storms and the strikes generated from them are mainly increasing around city fringes, in the surrounding suburbs.

—*Kim Long*

RIGHT: *Originally reported by the local Knoxville, Tennessee media as a tornado, meteorologists later concluded that this storm was what storm chasers call a "scud bomb." While they can look like tornadoes or microbursts, scud bombs are actually clouds created by thunderstorm outflow lifting saturated air, which, in this case, was just above the ground. The severe thunderstorm that served as the source of outflow for this rare looking scud bomb was dumping more rain more than five miles away. Photo: Terry Mosher*

FOLLOWING PAGES: *A ghostly white tornado writhes its way out of the sky near Emmetsburg, Iowa, on June 11, 2004. This tornado was part of an outbreak of more than 40 tornadoes spawned by a potent late-spring weather system that traversed portions of northern Iowa and southeastern Minnesota. Photo: Gene Rhoden*

LEFT: *A massive sandstorm blowing off the coast of the northwest African desert blankets hundreds of thousands of square miles of the eastern Atlantic Ocean with a dense cloud of Saharan sand. These storms and the rising warm air can lift dust 15,000 feet or so above the African deserts and then out across the Atlantic, many times reaching as far as the Caribbean. Recent studies have linked the decline of the coral reefs there to increasing frequency and intensity of these storms. Other studies show that Sahelian dust may play a role in determining the frequency and intensity of hurricanes in the eastern Atlantic Ocean. Photo: Orbimage*

RIGHT: *Ground temperature was nearing 100 degrees Fahrenheit when this large dust devil appeared in the Kalahari Gemsbok of South Africa. Dust devils occur most frequently on clear, hot days in the southwestern United States and in other desert areas around the world. Intense heating at the earth's surface produces sharp temperature contrast between the ground and the very lowest levels of the atmosphere, causing rapidly rising warm air to produce a mini-low pressure system. As the hot air rises, dust is picked up from the ground by a twisting motion caused by varying winds blowing into the system, or from frictional forces resulting from changing terrain. Photo: Stan Osolinski/Dembinsky Photo Associates*

WATER TWISTERS

In some parts of the world, waterspouts are a common sight. These twisting funnels of water are technically known as "convective vortices" and are similar to dust devils, which form over land. Most of the time, waterspouts occur on bodies of water with high surface temperatures, usually in tropical regions. The big spouts may generate vortices of 100 miles per hour or higher. In the ocean around the Florida Keys, as many as 500 waterspouts form every summer, some of them of the larger variety. Farther north, drivers crossing the Tampa Bay Bridge are frequently entertained by the sight of these dancing funnels during the summer months. Waterspouts are also sometimes observed in the Great Lakes, along the Gulf Coast, and in the southern part of the Pacific Coast. Several have also been noted on the Great Salt Lake in Utah.

Waterspouts form under a variety of conditions, but are mostly associated with the growth phase of cumulus congestus clouds. As a line of these clouds forms, waterspouts often follow, sometimes appearing in groups. A waterspout, visible because of the spinning spray of water that it is composed of, usually extends from the surface of a body of water up to the base of the cloud above it, typically only a few thousand feet above the surface. Often, the funnels formed by the smallest, most common waterspouts twist and snake unevenly across this distance. Depending on the amount of water in the funnel, all or part of the funnel may be observable. In general, the closer to the water, the more visible the funnel. As they form, waterspouts often kick up a circular movement of water near the surface, making a ring of spray at the base of the spout, which appears larger than the funnel that extends out of it. This feature is called the spray sheath. Because of long lines of visibility on the water, observers are often able to see the entire life cycle of a waterspout, beginning with the first signs of rotation on the surface. Waterspout funnels often grow in size as they "mature," and may form and reform more than once before dissipating. As spouts decay, they become thinner and fainter in appearance.

Most waterspouts are small, with thin, ropelike funnels that may only be a few feet in diameter, but sometimes much larger spouts are generated. The big ones feature higher rotation speeds and larger funnel diameters, sometimes as large as tornadoes. And just as tornadoes pack enough power to pose a threat to people and property, so too can large waterspouts produce damage and death, although this is rare.

117

Waterspouts in the Gulf of Mexico like this one near St. Petersburg Florida, draw up large columns of water as well as the associated inhabitants trapped in the updraft. Occasionally, waterspouts will move inland where they become tornadoes, releasing their load of fish and other sea creatures. The peak season for waterspout viewing in the Florida Keys is during the late summer months. Although usually smaller and weaker than land tornadoes, waterspouts have shown speeds of up to 190 miles per hour and should not be taken lightly. The best escape from a waterspout is at a right angle from its path. Photo: E. R. Degginger/Dembinsky Photo Associates

LAKE TAHOE WATER TWISTERS

On Lake Tahoe, high in the mountains in northern California, waterspouts are not common. In fact, waterspouts are so rare in mountain lakes that only a few have ever been recorded anywhere in the world. On September 26, 1998, however, the weather at Lake Tahoe (elevation 6,200 feet) featured a unique set of conditions ripe for the production of waterspouts.

These high-altitude twisters occurred between 7:00 and 9:30 A.M., forming and moving across the northern part of the lake. Several conditions combined to produce this event, although the exact set of circumstances is not known. One contributing factor may have been the surface temperature of the water, in the low 60s, but close to its peak temperature for the year in this high, cold environment. In these surroundings, the surface temperature rises due to the absorption of heat from the sun. At the same time, cyclonic circulation in the atmosphere of the region helped converge moisture at a relatively low altitude, related to an upper-level low, forming a line of cumulus congestus clouds and ideal conditions for the creation of waterspouts. Another potential factor may have been surface winds channeled by the local terrain around the shore of the lake.

A waterspout at Lake Tahoe is not only rare, the fact that there were at least six of these twisters observed makes it even more unusual. Stranger still, one of the spouts was of unusual size. This large funnel of vapor gradually expanded to be more than 250 feet in diameter and could have been a serious threat if it had encountered any boats or structures on shore. Before this event, only about 12 waterspouts had been reported on Lake Tahoe in the previous 30 years.

—*Kim Long*

Waterspouts over mountain lakes such as this one over Lake Tahoe are extremely rare. This waterspout occurred on the morning of September 26, 1998, approximately two miles off the Cal-Neva point. The sun line on the water is very close to the imaginary California-Nevada border that extends across Lake Tahoe. Tahoe Vista, California, is in the foreground and the Sierra Nevada mountain range is in the background. The depth of the lake in the area of the twister is well over 1,000 feet—one of the deepest parts of the lake. The diameter of the twister was about 275 feet with a spray of 500 feet across its base. Photo: Gary Kaufman

LEFT: *A rare waterspout in the Virgin Islands was formed when a cold front from the United States moved in and hit the warm tropical air. These waterspouts were coming up the East Gregory channel between Hassle Island on the left and Water Island on the right. St. Thomas is in the foreground. Photo: Gary Felton*

RIGHT: *Waterspouts are a dramatic sight during summer months in the Florida Keys as they form over water along the outer edges of heavy cloud build-ups. These large twin waterspouts formed in early summer just offshore Summerland Key, Florida. Lasting more than 30 minutes, the huge funnels put on a spectacular show for man and cormorant (in foreground) as they repeatedly rose and descended and crossed in front of each other. Photo: Ken Araujo*

THE NATURE OF HURRICANES

LEFT: *Hurricane Frances hits near Juno Beach, Florida, with hurricane force winds on September 4, 2004. Photo: Warren Faidley/Weatherstock*

ABOVE: *On August 28, 2005, while in the Gulf of Mexico, Hurricane Katrina reached Category 5 status, with maximum sustained winds near 175 miles per hour as it approached land the next day as a Category 3 storm. Photo: NOAA*

Hurricane. The word, derived from a Carib Indian phrase, means nothing more than "big wind." A hurricane is a big wind indeed, technically defined as a strong tropical cyclone with sustained winds of more than 74 miles per hour. But how that tropical cyclone got to spinning in the first place: well, that's a story, and one that scientists are still working on understanding.

In order to make a hurricane, nature has to bring together several disparate elements. First, there has to be an ocean, and at the surface of that ocean, the water must have attained a temperature of 82 degrees Fahrenheit (28° Celsius). Then there must be a clash of hot air and cold air, just the sort of thing that occurs when the cool waters of West Africa's Gulf of Guinea flow northward past the coast of Mauritania and Morocco and there meet the searing winds spilling off the Sahara Desert.

Air meets water, and water meets land, forming choppy waves that bounce back off the shoulder of the African continent. Those waves fuel the initial spin that sends a column of hot air, now moisture-laden, whipping upward. As this air rises, it cools rapidly, causing clouds of condensation to form and rain to fall. Given sufficient energy—and hurricanes are great engines that gather energy from near and far—the column of rising air will begin to turn cyclonically, moving with the prevailing winds and pulling up more and more warm water.

123

The power of the column builds. The barometric pressure drops, whence the term "tropical depression." The depression begins to generate ever more intense winds, while lightning crackles from the clouds and tall, long waves form below the growing storm system. The center of the vortex, the fair-weather eye of the storm, is calm, but all around it is weather that is anything but fair. As the storm nears land, the winds push water toward the shore. This "storm surge," as it is called, joins with the normal tides, creating the hurricane storm tide, a swell of water that is 15 or so feet higher than the normal water level and that causes trouble all on its own, quite apart from the furious winds that drive it.

Energy systems, the laws of thermodynamics advise, have a tendency to fall apart in time. Sometimes a hurricane can collapse under its own weight, hit cold water in the middle of the Atlantic, and go nowhere.

MONSOONS: MYTHS AND METEOROLOGY

A monsoon is simply defined as a seasonal shift in the pre-vailing wind direction, and is derived from the Arabic word for season, or *mausim*. For six months, the winter monsoon winds blow from the northeast, or offshore. This season is generally referred to as the dry season. During the summer monsoon or wet season, the prevailing winds are reversed and blow from the southwest, or onshore. This onshore flow brings moist oceanic air over the land, where it is forced to rise and create clouds and precipitation. The most intense monsoons are observed near the Arabian Sea, and consequently affect portions of southern Asia and India. It is here that some of the highest average rainfalls in the world are observed.

Monsoons are not restricted to India and the surround-ing Asian countries. Monsoon circulations are also observed in Europe, northern Australia, southern Africa, Chile, and even in the United States. The Desert Southwest experiences a dry and rainy season, attributable to a monsoon circulation off the Gulfs of Mexico and California. During the late summer months, moist tropical air is transported northward over the high desert terrain of northwest Mexico, Arizona, and New Mexico. This moist air acts as fuel for afternoon and evening thunderstorms over the mountains, and at night, these thun-derstorms occasionally move down to the lower-elevation desert valleys and produce some severe weather and flood-ing rains.

In the regions where the monsoon circulation is espe-cially well developed, seasonal precipitation is closely linked to the onshore and offshore flow. The summer monsoon, flowing onshore, brings moist oceanic air to the land. The air is forced to rise over the land, producing cloudiness and precipitation.

—*Gregory J. Stumpf*

Hail larger than softballs and winds estimated at 80 miles per hour rendered the tornadoes spawned by this powerful gust front insignificant by comparison. The supercell dropped many small tornadoes to the east of Turkey, Texas, causing little damage. Hail and wind from this storm, however, caused widespread damage in rural areas between Silverton and Childress, Texas. The orange coloration seen in the center background originated from the sun setting behind the storm. Although the orange-colored area appears to be rain-free, very large hail was falling within the area, making it a most dangerous place to be. Photo: Alan Moller

MAKING IT RAIN

Cloud seeding, making rain by scientific means, goes back just over 50 years, but making rain by unscientific means dates from antiquity. Just about every culture based on agriculture, especially those in arid regions or areas prone to drought, had some type of system aimed at influencing rain. These were typically based on the local religion and involved prayers, offerings, animal or human sacrifices, and other rituals. Modern rainmaking may be more successful than ancient methods, but its future is uncertain.

"Rainmaking" through hocus-pocus is an age-old scam. The late actor Burt Lancaster played Bill Starbuck in the 1956 movie *Rainmaker* (based on N. Richard Nash's stage play), which chronicled the con Starbuck perpetrated on drought-weary Three Point, Texas. The story of traveling rainmakers, though, goes back through centuries. Some were lucky enough to have retired in plenty; others, depending on the times and the circumstances, faced fates ranging from banishment, to prison, to death.

Although it's possible that some of these hucksters may have stumbled onto a practical method for inducing rainfall, the concept of making rain by scientific means is only about a half-century old. In the late 1940s, a General Electric experiment in a completely unrelated field led to the chance discovery that frozen carbon dioxide (dry ice) could turn supercooled water vapor into ice crystals. This phenomenon was isolated, and the first commercial applications began about 1950.

Moments before sundown on the Lamar River in the northeastern quadrant of Yellowstone National Park in Wyoming, a breathtaking rainbow appears. Within seconds of capturing the moment, a microburst knocked the photographer off his feet and sent his 10-pound tripod flying 20 feet through the air as the storm continued. Photo: Carter E. Gowl

These days, most rainmaking activity involves airplanes, but ground-based sprays can also be effective in some cases. In practice, a variety of different sprays are used, with silver iodide crystals being the most common. Applications are done from a variety of altitudes, depending on the specific nature of the cloud that is the target.

The effectiveness of cloud seeding, measured in laboratory settings as an increase in expected precipitation, range from 5 percent to 20–30 percent, with certain circumstances yielding increases of as much as 100 percent. In general, increases are heavier in summer months than in winter, when the technique is used to increase snowpacks for water supplies or skiing. Although an increase in rainfall is the most common use for the technology, it is also sometimes used to decrease potential hail damage and to reduce visibility-hampering fog.

The silver iodide used in most seeding activity is not believed to pose a health risk; silver and iodine, the two compounds produced by the process, are diluted far below any known risk threshold. Ice crystals can also be formed during seeding with dry ice, liquid propane, or compressed carbon dioxide. In warmer conditions, the technique may instead involve the use of compounds that attract water—urea, ammonium nitrate, and a variety of salts are the agents of choice in these conditions. For cloud seeding to work, other atmospheric and meteorological conditions must be favorable. That is, there should be enough existing moisture in the air at the intended altitude and the temperature must be within a certain range. These conditions, though, might be enough to produce rain on their own, so it is often difficult to measure or verify the benefits. To cloud-seeding clients, however, the potential rewards are clearly thought to be worth the expense.

143

A commonsense interpretation of cloud seeding suggests that the release of rain in a target area should be expected to "siphon off" rain from downwind areas. That is, if there is a given amount of moisture in the air, there should be less of it after a rain event. But those who seed clouds for a living point out that it is normal for areas downwind of the target area to also receive more rain. Depending on the geography, this is because the moisture content is constantly being replenished through evaporation from the ground.

Recently there has been increasing alarm, mostly from non-scientists, over what is called "contrail weather modification." The basic theory behind this concept is the known tendency for ice crystals to form more easily around existing ice crystals (as they do around dust or silver iodide crystals) than in clear air. With the increasing use of high-altitude aircraft and their resultant contrails, especially in high-volume commercial airways, this theory proposes that the contrails they produce increase the formation of ice crystals and clouds, changing regional weather patterns. After the terrorist attacks on September 11, 2001, all flights over the continental United States were grounded, providing a short test of the concept. The results, however, where not conclusive and both groups, those who subscribe to the theory and those who seek to debunk it, claimed victory.

Today's known and economically feasible technologies for cloud seeding may be widely used, but they are not devastatingly effective. Cloud seeding may work, but it doesn't work well enough to be a problem or a definitive solution. That may change, however, with breakthroughs in delivery or with another serendipitous technological discovery that improves reliability and efficiency. Tomorrow, the world may have to deal with the frightening possibility that freshwater could be literally plucked from the clouds before those clouds are ready to release it, changing global weather, crop distribution, and population concentrations.

—Tim Kern

RAINMAKING

Typical rain events release 10–15 percent of the existing moisture in the local atmosphere. An increase in precipitation through cloud seeding bumps this amount relatively little, to only as much as 20 percent of existing moisture.

1. The seeding compound acts on existing supercooled water droplets, causing them to freeze and initiating a chain of crystal-forming events that result in rainfall or snowfall.

2. The seeding activity and the formation of ice crystals release latent heat from the fusion process itself, raising the temperature of the surrounding cloud, thereby producing a larger cloud and a larger precipitation event.

FUTURE PROBLEMS

Cloud seeding, as the state of the art exists today, generates only small changes in local weather. Future gains in effectiveness, though, could raise moral and legal questions as the amount of water produced increases.

- Who owns the water in the clouds over a given area? Is it a person or a state?

- If water is pulled from clouds upwind and the region downwind suffers, what would be the legal liability on those who seeded the clouds?

- Thinking not only of the long-term effects of triggering drought downwind (and its consequences, such as forest fires and famine), what could happen in the "target" area if the seeding were too successful?

- Could widespread cloud seeding, over time, cause significant, near-permanent climatic damage?

- There's always "Mom's Rule," as well. All moms know it, in one form or another; it's a good rule to consider before making any major decision: "What if everybody did it? Would everybody be better off?"

WEATHER WOES DOWN ON THE FARM

LEFT: *A snow shower falls from "out of the blue," over a Lincoln County, Wisconsin farm. Radiant heat from the sun produced scattered clouds, some of which produced rain. But as the afternoon sun waned, unusually cool temperatures changed the rain to snow showers, producing the curious sight of an isolated cloud showering snow against a blue sky. For about a half hour, only a few of the clouds developed snow, as the clouds quickly dissipated when the temperatures dropped. Photo: David L. Sladky*

ABOVE: *Examples of "super-sized" hail displayed by some astonished residents. Photo: Courtesy of NCAR*

Hail threatens agricultural production worldwide. Once thought to be an unfavorable sign from the gods, it wreaks havoc from those Texas Panhandle fields and the Midwest all the way to China, sometimes leaving half a field in tatters and the other half untouched. In the United States, we often hear about the destruction of two big crops, corn and wheat, but hail also destroys citrus and other fruits, cotton, tobacco, tea, and vegetables. Although it's easy to believe that the bigger the hailstones are, the harder they fall, when it comes to crops, small hailstones—since there are more of them—can be more destructive than large ones, especially to tender young plants. One researcher estimates annual U.S. crop losses due to hail at $1.3 billion, a figure that represents 1 to 2 percent of the total annual crop value.

Hailstorms may deliver the wrong kind of precipitation, but it's the lack of precipitation that farmers fear most. The deadly killer down on the farm is drought. The official government definition for drought is "a period of insufficient rainfall for normal plant growth, which begins when soil moisture is so diminished that vegetation roots cannot absorb enough water to replace that lost by transpiration." Crop scientists also use other definitions based on meteorology, hydrology, and socioeconomics. And in some parts of the country, drought can also be linked to winter precipitation, because the snow that falls in the winter in the mountains is relied upon for irrigation in spring and summer months. Too little snow means not enough water for irrigation.

147

Over a period of a few years or more, a continuing drought can lead to a "Dust Bowl" stage in which the moisture content in the soil is seriously depleted, leading to a permanent loss of topsoil as it is blown away. Ranches also are hard hit by drought; water shortages reduce the amount of livestock that can be raised and bump up the cost of feed, often forcing the sale of animals for below-market value. Though measured in billions, the losses caused by drought to farming are hard to measure in simple dollars, because drought has such far-reaching effects in the social and economic fabric of a given region.

In crop losses for a single commodity (wheat), the recent drought in Colorado resulted in an estimated $100 million for the 2002 season, representing about half the value expected if precipitation were normal. Farmers can rely on "multiple-peril insurance"—only about 30 percent of farmers carried such insurance as of the mid-1990s—or government assistance in the form of low-interest loans, but during a drought cycle it's easy to become "loaned out."

Drought teaches lots of lessons: new conservation methods for soil and water; new farming techniques, such as crop rotation; and the development of more drought-resistant varieties of wheat and other crops. Precision farming applications, still experimental, use satellite-positioning technology to measure growth patterns and soil moisture. Sensors in equipment can regulate the amount of seed, fertilizer, and water for irrigation, varying these amounts if needed, from field to field or even within single fields, as recorded measurements dictate.

From too little to too much, flooding causes farmers all the serious problems regular homeowners face, and then some. The Great Flood of 1993 on the Mississippi River, which lasted from June through August and raged through 10 states, offers the best (or worst) recent example of farm woes from flooding. Total damage estimates range from $12 to 21 billion, but it's hard to identify the portion represented by agriculture, since no single government agency is responsible for systematically collecting or reporting flood-loss information. Service agencies and organizations that provide assistance also reveal problems faced on farms during a flood. There's more than just rotting crops, mold, fungus, and mildew to deal with; negative effects can also include the dilution of manure spreading into unwanted areas—including drinking water supplies, washed out feedlots, the saturation of stored grain, and water-damaged hay bales. And if the latter isn't damaging enough, spontaneous combustion can also occur from soaked hay overheating as it dries. After floods, danger lingers. Some fields may produce lower crop yields because of the altered chemical nature of saturated soil; seeds carried in by floodwaters can include those of new and different weeds; plant diseases linked to soil moisture increase; and tractors working sodden fields can over-compact the soil.

And then there are the rats and the mosquitoes. As the Mississippi floodwaters rose in 1993, an Iowa State University Extension wildlife specialist advised farmers to poison rats to prevent the spread of disease. Fields full of standing water create breeding grounds for mosquitoes and other disease-carrying insects that threaten livestock as well as humans. And if the thought of having to clean up the chainsaw after the basement's flooded makes you cringe, imagine what it would be like to recondition a sodden tractor or combine.

With the benefit of weather forecasting and flood warnings, today's farmers may be able to dodge more of Mother Nature's extremes than their predecessors. But even though tractors or livestock can be moved to safety, wheat, corn, and soybeans have no choice but to remain out in the open, vulnerable to weather woes, just as they have for thousands of years.

—*Kathleen Cain*

RIGHT: *A "high precipitation" (HP) supercell that occurred in the Texas Panhandle has considerable precipitation under its updraft base (left side of image) caused by light upper-level winds. The rain in these supercells falls closer to the updraft and is then pulled around the storm's base by the swirling mesocyclone, resulting in a menacing-looking rain-wrapped mesocyclone. This storm produced large hail, damaging winds, and several tornadoes that were difficult to see because of the dark precipitation. Photo: Alan Moller*

FOLLOWING PAGES: *The luck of the Irish was in Otjiwarongo, Namibia, Africa, when these lenticular clouds over the Omataco Mountains were photographed on St. Patrick's Day, 2004. These clouds were formed in a moist layer of stably stratified air that was forced to ascend when the wind flowed over the mountain. The rising air then cooled and formed clouds over the mountains when the temperature fell to the dew point. On the downwind side of the mountain, descending air forced the clouds to dissipate. Stable stratification suppressed vertical mixing of the air, so pronounced variations in moisture content occurred in narrowly separated layers. Photo: Viveca Venegas*

148

LUKE HOWARD:
THE MAN WHO NAMED THE CLOUDS

For millennia, clouds passed through the skies as interesting but nameless shapes. They were observed, painted, rhapsodized over in poems, books, plays, and sonnets. They were compared to animals and angels and described in terms of their form and color. But they had no names. Until an evening in December of 1802. That night, in London, a small society called the Askesians held one of its regular meetings. Luke Howard, a young pharmacist who had been fascinated by meteorology since childhood, read a paper to his fellow members in the society. His paper was entitled "On the Modifications of Clouds." Little did any of the people in this small group know the lasting and momentous effect this paper would have on the world of meteorology. In the paper, Howard gave Latin names to the most commonly seen clouds: cumulus, stratus, cirrus, and nimbus. Those names, while amended and added to over the years, still form the basis of cloud classification today.

Why did the naming of clouds occur so late in history? After all, clouds have been influencing human behavior and activities for eons, bringing rain, blocking sun, simply being there to be seen. The answer no doubt has to do with their ephemeral nature. Clouds appear and disappear; they change shape, move, or hang still. How could such amorphous objects be analyzed and classified with any reliability? How, in fact, could scientists be expected to take these whimsical forms very seriously at all? Scientists

Unique to the atmosphere of Australia, a Morning Glory cloud advances over the mangrove salt marshes of the Gulf of Carpentaria. These clouds may be up to 620 miles long and have a sculpted, undulating shape along their entire length. These giant clouds form seasonally when specific climate conditions interact with the unique geography of the region, most commonly when opposing sea breezes collide over the hot landmass of Cape York. When there is sufficient humidity, the cloud forms as humid air is forced up the front of the wave and condenses. On the descending edge of the wave, the cloud evaporates, creating the awesome effect of the entire cloud mass revolving backward, while advancing at 37 miles per hour. Photo: Barry Slade

look for order in the universe. The regular movements of heavenly bodies—stars, planets, the sun, and the moon—these were all worthy of scientific study. But a study of the capricious movements of clouds and storm systems? Not likely.

Given all that, it's understandable why astronomy preceded the development of meteorology by centuries. Yet in time, scientists' attention did turn to the weather around them, and to the clouds above them. As with any science, a number of inventions were essential before a systematic study could be undertaken. For meteorology, those inventions were the barometer and thermometer, which were in general use throughout the 18th century. During that century, many people with a curious nature began keeping weather diaries. By the end of the century, the laws governing the behavior of gases were becoming reasonably well understood, as was the nature of the sheath of air that surrounds the globe.

Scientists began to understand that the atmosphere did obey the laws of physics and chemistry, and that its future state could be predicted if its present and past states were accurately known. This implied careful measurement of the atmospheric variables of pressure, temperature, moisture, and wind, both at the surface and in the upper air. But for a true ability to predict weather and weather patterns, measurements would have to be made at many places over the globe, all at the exact same moment in time. For that to happen, meteorology had to wait until the latter part of the century and the invention of the telegraph to make precise timing possible.

Luke Howard was born in London on November 28, 1772. His father was a staunch Quaker, and young Luke attended a Friends grammar school near Oxford. It was here that he learned Latin, more Latin there than he would ever be able to forget, he commented later. His proficiency in the subject would play a tremendous role years later when he developed his classifications.

There is no doubt that the phenomenal weather year of 1783 was an important part of Howard's early fascination with clouds. In that year the young Howard, already a devoted observer of the universe, saw nature in a state of extreme agitation and turmoil. In May and June, violent volcanic eruptions shook

Iceland. The activity continued through the year, sending forth the greatest lava flow known to man. Great volumes of volcanic dust from the Eldeyjar eruption fell over Iceland and, carried by the westerly upper-level wind streams, spread over Scotland, destroying crops and killing livestock. The dust cloud eventually spread across England, continental Europe, and reached all the way to North Africa.

Meanwhile, another eruption was occurring on the other side of the world. In August, a volcano in Japan called Asamayama ejected boulders as large as houses and spewed enormous quantities of dust into the upper atmosphere. Westerly winds carried the dust around the whole Northern Hemisphere, which added to the general pall of haze. All the weather diaries of that period and even some of the great literary works of the day contain vivid references to the extended period of the "Great Fogg". The sense of under-lying uneasiness was heightened by major earth tremors in Calabria and Sicily.

Finally, and most gloriously, on August 18 a large fiery meteor flashed across the skies of Western Europe. It was seen by tens of thousands of people, including young Luke Howard. There can be little doubt of the effect these events had on a 10-year-old boy who was already cloud-struck.

With his school days behind him, Howard became apprenticed to a chemist in Stockport. He endured years of drudgery as he ground chemical preparations, cleaned bottles, and swept floors. He satisfied his intellectual cravings after hours, by studying French, botany, and chemistry. Eventually he became a pharmacist and opened his own business in London. Soon he became friends with other young men with similar interests in scientific matters. One particularly close friend was William Allen, who owned a successful commercial pharmacy. He hired Howard to run his manufacturing laboratory in Plaistow, just outside London. As Howard traveled back and forth between London and Plaistow, he had ample time to continue his studies of cloud forms.

It was Allen who decided, in March of 1796, to establish a society for the discussion of scientific matters. This society was dubbed the Askesians, from the Greek *askesis*, which means, roughly, intellectual exercise. The meetings were held every other week at 6:00 p.m., and the rules required that each member prepare a paper on a subject of interest, and read it before the society, in rotation, or pay a fine.

While Howard was thoroughly engaged with the Askesians, he was also doing a great deal of scientific study on his own. He was particularly impressed with the work of Swedish taxonomist Carl von Linné, known more familiarly as Linnaeus. Linnaeus had established the beginnings of the modern system of classification of all life forms, a system scientists around the world would eventually adopt.

Howard presented a number of papers during the six years that he had been a member of the Askesians, but it was the paper that he presented on an evening in December 1802 that ensured his reputation. His lecture, "On the Modifications of Clouds," was a brilliant exposition of a scheme he had developed for classifying and naming clouds. It was the culmination of Howard's years of observation. Two centuries later, we are still using the essence of his scheme.

Howard proposed in his paper that it was possible to identify a number of simple categories within the complexity of the changing skies. He set out to establish a complete classification that would cover all possible cases. Like Linnaeus, he used Latin names, a language that fortuitously transcends national boundaries. He put clouds in four groups:

Cumulus (Latin for heap) Convex or conical heaps, increasing upward from a horizontal base

Stratus (Latin for layer) Widely extended horizontal sheets

Cirrus (Latin for curl of hair) Fibers that can stretch in any or all directions

Nimbus (Latin for rain) Systems of clouds from which rain falls

One of the principal insights in Howard's essay is his insistence that clouds are a proper subject for research and theory. He noted that clouds have many shapes but only a few basic forms. Those shapes and forms are caused by water present in the atmosphere, water that may be in any or all of its three states: liquid droplets, solid ice crystals, or gas (water vapor). He noted, too, that while circulating air causes unstable conditions in the atmosphere, the principles of cloud formation are still understandable and are capable of being classified and studied scientifically. Howard's other important assertion was that clouds can change from one form to another. A cumulus cloud may flatten and widen into a stratus formation. Simple observation shows that clouds move, but Howard contributed the knowledge that they change and merge. They are not fixed in one form for easy classification and study.

Even though the physics of air and water vapor were poorly understood in Howard's day, his analysis had a sound physical basis, and his paper was met with acclaim. It was soon published in Alexander Tilloch's *Philosophical Magazine*, a major disseminator of scientific knowledge. Before long Howard's paper was reprinted in a number of various journals and encyclopedias, both in England and on the Continent.

Howard continued his studies of meteorology, and his work included many significant achievements. In 1806, he began his Meteorological Register, which was published regularly by *Athenaeum Magazine*. He wrote the first book on urban climatology, *The Climate of London,* published in two volumes in 1818–19. In it he wrote of the impact that cities can have on meteorological conditions. For example, he carefully described London's famous fog, and noted that there could be almost no visibility in the city while a few miles away the atmosphere was clear. This seems very obvious today and not particularly noteworthy, but smog, as we call city fog today, was an unknown concept in the early 19th century.

In 1821, Howard was elected a Fellow of the prestigious Royal Society, for his contributions to meteorology. In the second half of Howard's life, he became more involved with his chemical manufacturing business—though his interest in clouds never flagged. His long life ended on March 21, 1864. At his funeral, his son said, "A beautiful sunset was a real and intense delight to him; he would stand at the window, change his position, go out of doors and watch it to the last lingering ray." Clouds in all their many moods carried an endless fascination for the man who invented their names.

Eventually, a list of 10 cloud types was drawn up, expanding on Howard's four.

Cumulus, Stratus, Cirrus, Nimbus, Cirrostratus, Cirrocumulus, Stratocirrus, Cumulocirrus, Stratocumulus, Cumulonimbus

With minor revisions, these appeared in the 1896 *International Cloud Atlas* and are still in use today.

Luke Howard was untrained in meteorology, a chemist and pharmacist by profession, yet through his never-ending curiosity and masterful powers of observation, he left an indelible mark on the world around him. Some call him, with good reason, the Godfather of Clouds.

—*John A. Day*

TEN REASONS TO LOOK UP

1. Clouds and cloudscapes are the greatest free show on earth. It doesn't cost a penny to look up and feast your eyes on the view.

2. Clouds are never exactly the same. While there are four basic cloud types (cumulus, stratus, cirrus, and nimbus), nature combines them to compose endless symphonies in the skies.

3. Many skies are simply beautiful to behold. There is no other way of saying it. The gradations of light and color in the late afternoon and very early morning hours are bouquets for the eye.

4. Clouds are a billboard of Coming Attractions. While it takes a skilled eye to interpret the messages on the billboard, there is a feeling of immense satisfaction when one's own forecast is verified.

5. Observing the sky at regular intervals makes one feel connected to nature.

6. Cloud watching promotes a global consciousness. Weather satellites bring large-scale images of cloud patterns into our homes. They help us realize that "our" clouds are connected to other clouds all around the world.

7. The earth is unique because of its vast amounts of water. Clouds are made of water and are a constant reminder of its importance.

8. Water is a miracle substance. Scientists have found that simple H_2O is anything but simple. Those H_2O molecules link together and bring us the glorious clouds above us. Without water, there would be no clouds.

9. Cloud watching is an antidote to boredom. Clouds are ever changing, ever evocative.

10. Clouds are a magic show. Where do they come from, and where do they go? This is a mystery to the nonscientist, and an area of endless fascination.

— *John A. Day*

Luke Howard: The Man Who Named the Clouds and Ten Reasons to Look Up reprinted with permission from The Book of Clouds, by John A. Day, © Sterling Publishers Co., Inc.

UNUSUAL CLOUD TYPES

1. VIRGA: As rain clouds gather, if you see a tail or curtain or veil of cloud flowing beneath them, or the rain looks as if it is walking above the horizon, it may be the virga slipping away through the sky. Although it can develop any place where precipitation occurs, it is most likely to develop in drier climates like Denver, Colorado. The nearby mountain barrier robs the low-level atmosphere of moisture, making the air even drier beneath the clouds. When the moisture leaves the upper atmosphere and descends in the form of the serpentine virga, its chances of evaporating before it reaches the ground are much higher.

2. MAMMATUS: They are often seen near the back edge of strong to severe thunderstorms. They are farmed by packets of "reverse" convection, i.e., the downward acceleration of air parcels. These pockets create the downward protrusions within the thunderstorm clouds.

3. IRIDESCENT: The iridescence is seen as a patchwork of pastel color throughout the clouds, and is produced by the diffraction of sunlight traveling through various-sized cloud droplets.

4. KELVIN-HELMHOLTZ WAVES: These delicate wave clouds are also referred to as billows. They occur when the wind velocity changes rapidly with height, resulting in breaking waves, similar to what occurs at the beach. When enough moisture is present within the rising-motion portion of these waves, then condensation occurs, thus allowing us to see these waves. In dry conditions, the waves are still present but occur in clear air. Kelvin-Helmholtz waves are the principal cause of clear-air turbulence for aircraft.

5. CUMULONIMBUS: The cauliflower-like portion of this thunderstorm cloud beneath the flat anvil represents the region of the storm where air is rapidly ascending in an unstable atmosphere. Here, the cloud is composed of supercooled water droplets, or water in its liquid state in a subfreezing environment. The flat ice-crystal anvil cloud forms at the base of the stable stratosphere, often eight miles high or higher, where the cauliflower updrafts from beneath lose their buoyancy and spread horizontally.

6. LENTICULAR: A very smooth, round or oval, lens-shaped cloud that is often seen, singly or stacked in groups, near or in the lee of a mountain ridge. These clouds are caused by a wave wind pattern created by the mountains. They are also indicative of downstream turbulence on the leeward side of a barrier.

—Kathleen Cain

LEFT: *South of Beloit, Kansas, a contrail billows in the evening.*
Photo: Charles A. Doswell III

VIRGA *Photo: Jeff Foott/Getty Images*

MAMMATUS *Photo: Jorn Olsen*

IRIDESCENT CIRRUS *Photo: Warren Faidley/Weatherstock*

KELVIN-HELMHOLTZ WAVES *Photo: Brooks Martner*

CUMULONIMBUS *Photo: Ricahrd Kaylin/Getty Images*

LENITCULAR CAP CLOUD *Photo: Stan Osolinski/Dembinsky Photo Associates*

COASTAL FOG:
BEAUTIFUL AND DEADLY

PRECEDING PAGE 158: *A classic lenticular cloud is captured in the Sierra Nevada outside Reno just minutes before the onset of a windstorm so severe that it cracked the windows and stripped the paint off the photographer's car. Photo: Kathleen Norris Cook*

PRECEDING PAGE 159: *The hanging, pillow-like pouches underneath the anvil top of certain cumulonimbus clouds (mammatus clouds) like these in Weld County, Colorado, indicate severe turbulence. Photo: Gregory Thompson*

LEFT: *A ridge of Claremont Canyon rises over the fog-draped San Francisco Bay. Photo: Galen Rowell/Mountain Light*

ABOVE: *A pillow of fog rests below Mt. Edgecumbe, in Sitka Sound, Alaska. Photo: Fred Hirschmann*

It is difficult to understand how something that inspires so much romance can also create so much havoc. No wonder that the word fog also means an uncertain or confused position.

Fog is formed by the condensation of water vapor on condensation nuclei, microscopic dust particles that are always present in natural air. This condensed water vapor in cloudlike masses lying close to the ground is sufficiently dense to reduce horizontal visibility to less than 3,281 feet (1,000 meters). As soon as the humidity of the air exceeds saturation by a fraction of 1 percent, fog occurs. Coastal fog, like that common in San Francisco, is technically known as "advection fog." As the warm, moist air moves over cold surfaces, it is cooled below the dew point, the temperature at which dew forms. Fog will occur either when the moisture content of the air is increased beyond the saturation point or when the air is cooled below the dew point, causing the excess moisture to condense and form fog.

The advection fog that is common along the Pacific Coast· in summer comes from warm, moist air that is carried by the wind from warmer waters off shore. When the warm air reaches the surface waters near the coast, the air cools and condenses due to a seasonal upwelling this region of the ocean experiences, which pushes colder water to the surface. After the sun has had a chance to penetrate the fog and warm the earth, the conditions are altered, and the fog disappears.

The two major coastal fog areas in the United States are the Pacific Coast region and the New England region. San Francisco does get lots of fog—more than 18 days of solid, heavy fog are recorded on an average each year—but San Francisco is not the foggiest place on the West Coast. Cape Disappointment, Washington, located at the mouth of the Columbia River, earns this title. Here, the average is 2,552 hours of heavy fog a year. That translates to nearly 106 days of fog. Who do you think had the honor of naming this community? A disgruntled fisherman, no doubt.

On the East Coast, the foggiest area is along the Maine coastline. Moose Peak Lighthouse, altitude 72 feet, is situated on Mistake Island, where they average 1,580 hours of heavy fog a year. No wonder the waters

161

LEFT: *Spawned by a glacier in the Antarctic, this iceberg drifted north of the South Sandwich Islands and was quickly being destroyed by the inhospitable climate of the Southern Ocean. Waves crash against the iceberg and cascade 20 feet into the cold waters below. The blue color is the result of dense glacial ice refracting light so that all colors except for blue are absorbed. Pintado petrel birds float below looking for tidbits of food stirred up by the turbulent seas. Photo: Colin McNulty/Small World Images*

RIGHT: *Researchers take an October dip into the Ross Sea to explore this iceberg, run aground at a depth of 84 feet, just south of Cape Evans on Ross Island. In the Antarctic, all life revolves around the ice. The iceberg shelf is covered in ice algae and loaded with bright red amphipods grazing for food, who in turn attract large numbers of hungry ice fish. Larval fish by the thousands rise and fall along the anchor ice. Photo: Norbert Wu*

FOLLOWING PAGES: *Altocumulus clouds are reflected in the iceberg-strewn ocean at the mouth of the Weddell Sea. Close to the Antarctic coast, it can be very calm, especially inside the belt of pack ice that can dampen the swells. Photo: Jonathan Chester*

CLIMATE CHANGE

GLOBAL WARMING, GLACIAL MELTING, DESERTIFICATION, AND POLLUTION

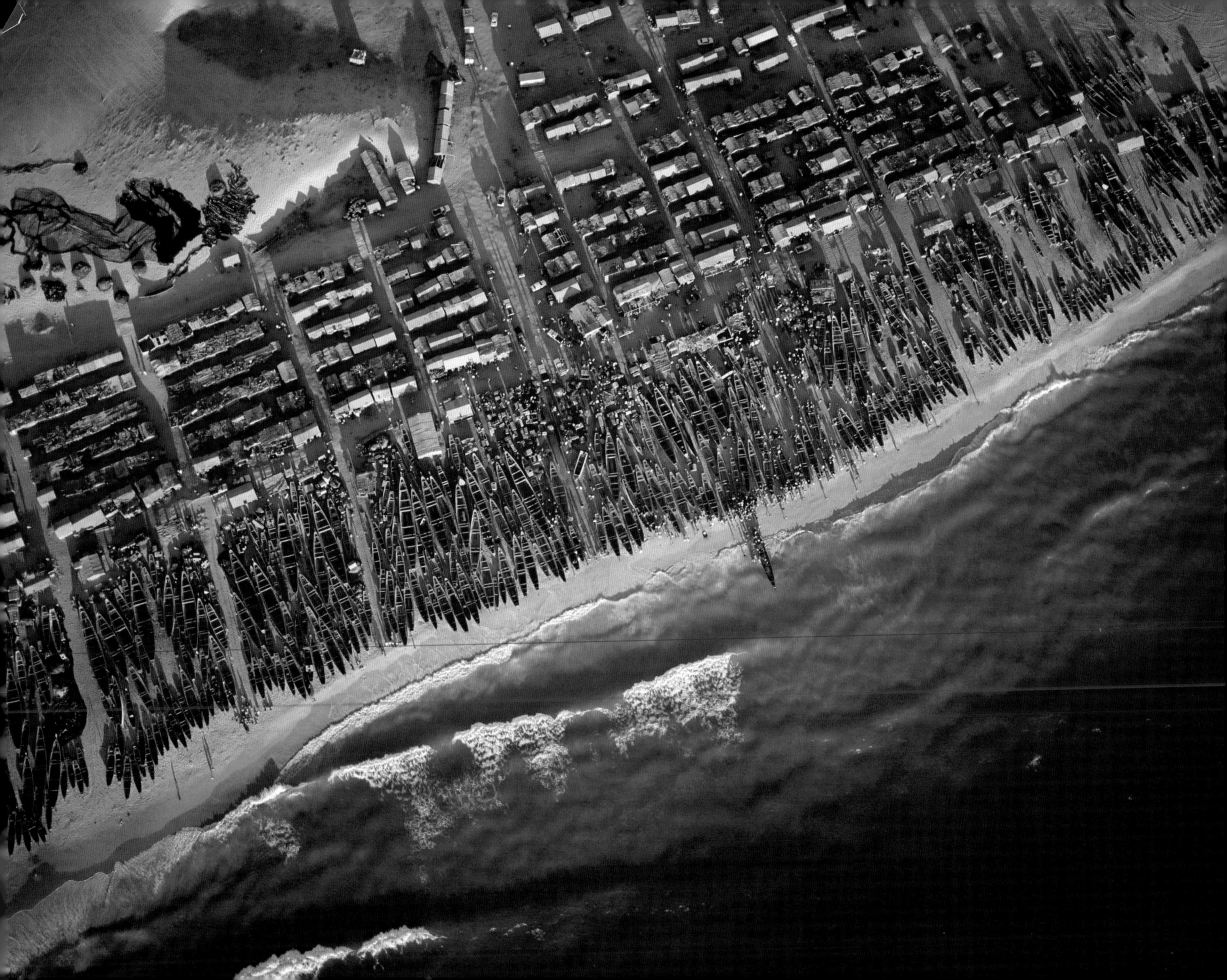

The old joke in meteorology school use to be: "Climate is what you expect; weather is what you get." Trouble is, climate, once thought of as an unchanging mean about which fluctuations would bounce, is now anything but unchangeable, even on the scale of humankind's existence on earth, and now even for an individual lifetime. Truth be said, climate has always been changing, long before humans showed up and picked fights with wooly mammoths and saber-toothed tigers. Continents have wandered—witness oil under the Arctic sea and coal beds in the Antarctic. Meteorologists once attempted to measure the "solar constant" of incoming energy which actually fluctuates sufficiently to alter climate. Volcanic eruption dust clouds cause "years without a summer." Once humans abandoned the earth-centric notion of the universe, we were comforted by a predictable elliptical orbit around the sun, except that the ellipse varies on the scale of tens to hundreds of thousands of years while the planet wobbles on its axis like a crazy top, inducing all manner of climate cycles.

When Homo sapiens showed up and started burning fossil fuels and changing the landscape, these were seemingly small change in the grand scheme of things. Then late-19th-century rises in carbon dioxide levels caused a few scientists to start thinking about greenhouses. But how could mere humanity change the climate of an entire planet? Surely Mother Earth would be more resilient than that? We once thought we couldn't pollute a river—until Ohio's Cuyahoga caught fire. We once thought we couldn't pollute our atmosphere—until acid rain soured our lakes, giant brown clouds of Asian dust crossed the Pacific, and smog blobs choked the air over the eastern U.S. on hot summer days. We couldn't pollute the oceans—until hypoxic "dead zones" appeared at the Mississippi's mouth, and six-pack holders floated in mid-Pacific along with thousands of rubber duckies from container spills off giant cargo vessels.

But change climate? The upward march of atmospheric carbon dioxide levels is unquestioned and unrelenting as we burn ever more fuel. Beyond CO_2, heat-trapping methane emerges from pastures of grazing cows, bucolic rice paddies, and melting arctic permafrost. Mother Earth—or the Sun-Earth-Ocean System as some call it—is responding to both natural and human-induced changes in ways both measurable and still unpredicted. Humanity is clearly conducting an uncontrolled experiment on its own atmosphere. Sea level creeps upwards, Greenland meltwater flows ever faster, spring comes earlier and earlier in mid-latitudes, and polar bears searching for ice floes become iconic images, just as did the breathtaking portrait taken from the Apollo capsule of Spaceship Earth rising over the moon. Our spaceship. The one on which we must all keep traveling, at least for a long, long time.

The stern prose of the Information Statement on Climate Change by the American Meteorological Society tells it all: "Despite the uncertainties noted above, there is adequate evidence from observations and interpretations of climate simulations to conclude that the atmosphere, ocean and land surface are warming; that humans have significantly contributed to this change and that further climate change will continue to have important impacts on human societies, on economies, ecosystems and wildlife through the 21st century and beyond ... [I]n the next 30 years, increasing air temperatures will reduce snow pack, shift snow melting, reduce crop production and rangeland fertility and cause continued melting of the ice caps and sea level rise." What have we children of earth done? Is this any way to treat our Mother?

—*Walter Lyons, CCM*

Fishing boats line the once deserted shore of what is probably the fastest growing city in Africa. Before independence in 1960, Nouakchott was a small coastal oasis supporting 15 families in mud houses. Now, over 700,000 people have flocked to this capital city to seek wealth and refuge from desertification of their traditional grazing lands. As their herds of livestock vanished, fishing has become a major part of the national economy. Mauritanian waters were once the richest fishing grounds in Africa, but with rampant overfishing by large offshore trawlers, fish populations are now only 30 percent of what they were 20 years ago. Photo: George Steinmetz/Corbis

185

MEASURING ICE

Scientists use a variety of methods to measure the Arctic icepack. Submarines roving in the sea under the floating ice direct their sonar upward to measure ice thickness; the reflected signal changes according to the thickness. Ice breakers also participate by measuring the thickness of pieces of ice broken and scattered by their passage. Records from previous voyages are compared to show changes due to weather and over time. The best measures for ice coverage in the Arctic sea come from satellites, which can distinguish the long-wave radiation emitted by sea ice from heat that is emitted by water.

ON THIN ICE

"Strange as it seems, the Arctic ice is melting at so precipitous a rate that scientists now believe that the Northwest Passage may be navigable by regular ships for part of the year, or even all of it, in as little as 10 to 15 years."—*Toronto Globe and Mail, February 5, 2000*

The explorers who exhausted themselves searching for the Northwest Passage might be heartened to know they were not wrong, just 500 years too early. Perhaps no area on earth will be as affected by global warming as much as the Arctic. The Intergovernmental Panel for Climate Change says temperatures have increased nine degrees Fahrenheit on average in the Arctic over the past century, and they predict temperatures will continue to rise more there than anywhere else on earth.

According to the Nansen Environmental and Remote Sensing Area in Norway, the ice cover decreased about three percent every 10 years between 1978 and 1996. The thickness of the ice decreased an average of 42 percent in all the main areas of the Arctic Ocean between the periods 1958–1976 and 1993–1997.

The perennial ice—ice that has survived one summer or more—has shrunk more than twice as fast as the total ice cover, according to Nansen scientists. Put another way, as the winter freeze adds a little less ice each season, the net effect of seasonal melting is that the thicker, semi-permanent base gradually decreases.

Two University of Bergen researchers summed it up this way: "What is completely certain is that if the trend in the ice cover and the ice thickness does not level off soon, the perennial ice in the Arctic will disappear by the end of this century. In other words, the entire Arctic will be free of ice during the summer months."

— *Randy Welch*

LEFT: *There is sufficient melting on the surface of the Sorsdal Glacier in summer to have streams coalesce into a river ending in a spectacular waterfall that plunges hundreds of feet into the ocean. The Sorsdal is one of the key outlet glaciers that contribute to the drainage of the East Antarctic ice sheet. Photo: Jonathan Chester*

RIGHT: *Closed pack ice occurs in the spring when wind and currents break up the fast ice and move the frozen plates into a tight band of floating ice. These might be anywhere from a few hundred yards to miles in extent. This tight formation makes passage impossible for all but an icebreaker, but ice charts that are compiled daily from satellite imagery give ships' captains the means to avoid or minimize the problem. Photo: Jonathan Chester*

DESERTIFICATION

LEFT: *A sandstorm on a dirt road between Douentza and Timbuktu in Mali. Photo: Remi Benali/Corbis*

ABOVE: *A Chinese villager waters a tree planted to combat desertification on a hill. China, the second largest source of greenhouse gases after the United States, is one of the world's worst affected countries by desertification. Photo: Diego Azubel/epa/Corbis*

Study a physical map of the world. As you follow the tropics of Cancer and Capricorn, 23.5 degrees on either side of the equator, you will see a brown band of deserts circling the planet. They lie in the "horse latitudes," where constant high-pressure systems separate the westerly and trade winds, driving away the rain clouds. Some of those dry lands, like the Atacama of Chile, the Namib and Kalahari deserts of southern Africa, and the western Australian desert, are the result of cold ocean currents that divert rain-laden air away from coastlines. Others, like the Mojave and Sonoran deserts of California, Arizona, and Mexico and the deserts of central and eastern Australia, are caused by the "rain-shadow effect," through which coastal mountains milk rain from the air before it passes inland. Still others, like the Gobi and Taklamakan deserts of Mongolia and China, are simply so far away from the ocean that the winds lose any moisture they may hold long before reaching the distant continental interior.

201

The world's desert systems are harsh environments. By definition, a desert receives less than 10 inches of unevenly distributed rain throughout the year, though it need not suffer extreme hear. (Antarctica, for example, is a desert where rain never falls and no vegetation grows.) These deserts now cover some 20 percent of the planet's surface, a figure that grows each year, thanks to the phenomenon of desertification, a process of soil erosion and land degradation that occurs when land that normally receives little rain is stripped of whatever vegetation it has.

Desertification results from several natural processes that are harmless enough one by one but can play ecological havoc in combination. One is the ongoing process of global warming, which is altering weather patterns around the world, bringing drought to once temperate zones. Another is the desiccating El Niño weather system in the Pacific, which has been prevalent for much of the past decade and has led to a virtual stop of summer rain in the deserts of North and South America.

But the most powerful agent of desertification is humankind. With the growing world population, formerly marginal areas on the fringes of deserts are becoming more heavily settled. With humans come livestock, which devour the already scant ground vegetation; taller trees and shrubs are cleared away for fuel wood. The removal of plant life means that when rain falls, it cannot penetrate the dry soil, once broken by plant roots; instead, it runs off the surface toward low ground in a process that hydrologists call "sheet flooding." In the last quarter century, according to United Nations statistics, at least 128,000 people have died as a result of such floods.

Desertification has caused tremendous social change in affected areas, especially in sub-Saharan Africa and Central America, where famine is now a constant danger and massive flooding and mudslides follow even modest rainfall. In these areas, desertification has caused the destruction of rural agriculture and a massive migration of country people into already crowded cities.

Desertification has emerged as a major environmental problem in some unlikely areas. In the deserts of the United States, areas that have been intensively grazed and farmed have grown a thick skin of salts and other minerals, making the land useless for further agriculture. In Beijing, dust storms from the nearby Gobi are a regular hazard, while the Gobi's sand dunes advance toward the city at a rate of as much as 15 miles a year. In Italy, Spain, and elsewhere in the Mediterranean, intensive olive farming has led to soil erosion and canyon-cutting, and great areas of land are now unsuitable for agriculture.

Desertification is not unstoppable, but containing its spread will require massive international efforts and cost trillions of dollars. Any measures to halt its growth will involve continued economic hardship for the people most affected by desertification, for they include putting an end to livestock grazing and irrigated agriculture until plant cover has returned to a denuded stretch of ground, a process that can take decades. International aid organizations are working to convert farmers and herders in places like the Sahel of West Africa and northwestern India into modern-day Johnny Appleseeds, planting hedgerows and windbreaks to halt the advancing sands. The fate of hundreds of millions of lives and of millions of acres hinges on their success or failure.

—Gregory McNamee

ABOVE: *In Ningxia province, the lack of water has forced peasants to collect snow to stock in underground reservoirs. The central government launched a program called "Mother Cellar" which aims to build underground storehouses capable of holding water for several months. The desertification of this region is extreme and there are no wells or trees. Snowfall is greeted with relief by the locals. The only form of revenue for families is tree planting with saplings ordered by the government for reforestation purposes. Other than the water from the underground storehouses, the only way to access water is for peasants to buy water delivered by trucks. Photo: Yves Gellie/Corbis*

THE BURIAL OF BEIJING

For most of the people of the world, desertification is something that happens far away from home. But in Beijing, the phenomenon is much more real, creating serious problems in this massive city, home to about 11 million people. Sand, dirt, and dust originating in the shifting deserts of northwestern China are now frequent visitors here. Many residents now dread the spring, when annual conditions trigger multiple sandstorms. In 2000, as many as a dozen sandstorms struck the city during the spring months, and for some observers, the intensity seemed worse than in previous years. During such storms, visibility is reduced and breathing can be difficult; during peak storm periods, airports are closed and hospitals fill with casualties of the wind-borne muck.

Not only is this "muck" a visible sign of desertification, the sand dunes themselves are also on the march. Scientists measure their progress southward toward Beijing at about 2.1 miles per year—some measurements put the movement as high as 15.5 miles a year. The small city of Huailai, which is currently being enveloped by these dunes, has recently had a name change. It is now called Sand City.

The Chinese are not just studying this menace; they are making plans to protect Beijing. One effort is the planting of large numbers of trees about 112 miles north of the city, in Hebei province, where desertification is particularly intense. Bans are also in place to prevent the harvesting of black moss, a natural ground cover, and to limit the cultivation of ground for agriculture in sensitive areas.

—Gregory McNamee

LEFT: *A worker carries hay used to prevent desertification at the edge of the expanding Maowusu Desert. Sand dunes are encroaching as a result of grazing livestock and constant drought in one of China's poorest regions. China spends about 2 billion yuan ($280 million) annually to prevent desertification, which affects 2.64 million square kilometers. Twenty percent of China's total landmass is desert. Photo: Michael Reynolds/epa/Corbis*

THE WORLD'S LARGEST DESERTS

Sahara	Northern Africa	3.5 million sq. mi.
Gobi	China	500,000 sq. mi.
Patagonia	Southern Argentina	300,000 sq. mi.
Rub al-Khali	Southern Arabia	250,000 sq. mi.
Kalahari	Southern Africa	225,000 sq. mi.
Chihuahuan	Mexico/southwestern US	175,000 sq. mi.
Great Sandy	Western Australia	150,000 sq. mi.
Great Victoria	Southwestern Australia	150,000 sq. mi.
Gibson	Western Australia	120,000 sq. mi.
Kara Kum	Turkmenistan	120,000 sq. mi.
Syrian	Northern Arabia	100,000 sq. mi.
Thar	India	100,000 sq. mi.

Desert areas are very approximate because clear physical boundaries may not occur.

TOP LEFT: *Signs of desertification are apparent in fields located on the outskirts of the city of Segou, Mali. Photo: Remi Benali/Corbis*

BOTTOM LEFT: *A dead bull on a dry plain in central Mali is evidence that life in Africa's Sahel is becoming increasingly difficult. Desertification and rising temperatures due to climate change are making farming nearly impossible and the survival of livestock of critical concern. Photo: Nic Bothma/epa/Corbis*

RIGHT: *A Touareg man fills jerrycans with water from one of the few wells in working order. Thirty years of drought have seriously affected the equilibrium and daily lives of northern tribes in Mali. The progressive disappearance of watering holes and the advance of the desert have pushed tribal populations to installations on the periphery of towns. Photo: Bruno Fert/Corbis*

CHINA, COAL & GLOBAL POLLUTION

LEFT: *A coal power plant spews toxic fumes into the atmosphere in Hebei province, China. Photo: Liu Liqun/Corbis*

ABOVE: *A migrant worker shovels coal at a depository in the outskirts of Beijing. By the end of 2007, Beijing will completely ban all such small privately operated coal depositories in efforts to reduce the capital's notorious air pollution before hosting the 2008 Olympics. Despite government pledges to curb environmental pollution, China's economy heavily relies on coal to meet growing energy demands. Photo: Michael Reynolds/epa/Corbis*

What goes up, the adage has it, must come down. It's an old law of the universe, and universally recognized. Even so, when in 2004 a professor of atmospheric sciences at Harvard University, Daniel Jacob, published the results of a study of a local weather phenomenon, it surprised many New Englanders. Jacob announced that a plume of polluted air that had been hanging in the region's skies had drifted all the way from China, barely affected by the moderating and buffeting winds of the jet stream. The smoky cloud's endurance was bad enough, but it was also full of mercury and other highly toxic materials given off by the burning of coal, among them sulfur dioxide, nitrogen oxide, and sooty particulates.

Two years later, in April 2006, a thick cloud of smoke that had been hanging over heavily industrial northern China blew away, as if unmoored from earth. It settled over Korea for a few days, enveloping Seoul in a thick blanket, and then sailed across the Pacific, making landfall in California a few days later. The cloud was so thick that satellites could track it from far above earth, as if it were a landmass. Only when it hit the tall barrier of the Sierra Nevada did the cloud begin to break up, shedding sulfur, mercury, and other by-products of coal burning into Lake Tahoe.

Coal smoke has been an atmospheric problem for as long as coal has been used as a fuel. Londoners of a certain age still remember the deadly winter inversions that once choked the city in coal smoke and fog, giving rise to the word "smog." The "forest death" that visited so many Old World woodlands in the 1970s and 1980s was largely the product of the coal-burning industries of northern Europe, just as the "acid rain" of the Eastern Seaboard owed its existence to coal-burning plants there. Recognizing the dangers wrought by coal, the nations of the industrialized world developed filtering systems that scrubbed the smoke emerging from industrial smokestacks, even as most consumers switched over to natural gas and other cleaner heating fuels.

Yet today, a third of America's lakes are so polluted with mercury that warnings are issued against eating fish taken from them. One-half of that mercury, it is estimated, comes from China, whose factories and power plants release nearly 600 tons of it into the atmosphere every year, along with 22.5 million tons of sulfur.

207

FEBRUARY

1 1916: Seattle, WA, averages less than 10" of snow a season. Today's 21.5" snowfall was not only several average years of snow, but the city's all-time 24-hour record snowfall. Transportation in western WA was crippled.

2 1976: An explosively deepening low pressure (unofficially to 27.9" in Wiscasset, ME) caused a storm surge to come up Penobscot River; water was 12' deep in downtown Bangor in 15 minutes; 200 cars disappeared in the icy water. Heroic rescues kept death toll to 0.

3 1982: A home near Panama City, FL, was set on fire by lightning. Gas leaking from a gas line damaged by the lightning ignited; the resulting explosion destroyed the house. Amazingly, none of the 4 people in the house were hurt.

4 2006: Winds to 78 mph (produced by an offshore 968 mb 28.6" low) raked northwest WA. The Hood Canal Bridge and Evergreen Floating Bridge were closed; ferry service ceased. Seattle's Woodland Park Zoo was closed due to concern falling trees might smash fences and release animals.

5 2001: 18" of snow in FL, with snowfall rates exceeding 4" per hour. Schools and businesses closed because of the storm. It did happen, but this Florida is in MA. Parts of western MA were buried under 1 to 2' of snow. Storm totals included 23" at Savoy and 18" at Florida.

6 2006 (6–15): Extreme and severe drought conditions over most of AZ. A wildfire started by an abandoned campfire on the Mogollon Rim 12 miles north of Payson burned 4,200 acres before being contained. The same area normally has 12+" of snow this time of year.

7 1998 (4–7): Up to 4.5" rain fell on saturated soils of north/central GA (2–4); resultant flooding caused up to 20' rises on rivers/creeks. In Laurens County, a close call. 11 children evacuated safely from a stalled school bus before it floated down the Oconee River.

8 1957 (7–9): Ice storms in HI? A general 3" of clear ice collected on surfaces at the top of Mt. Haleakala, Maui (elevation: 10,000'). Three miles of power lines toppled. Wind gusts to 100 mph; coldest temperatures 24°F.

9 2006: Death Valley, CA, is the hottest (and driest) location in the U.S., having reached 134°F on July 10, 1913 (only 2°F less than the world's record high). Today's 90°F high is its earliest ≥90°F of record (records began in 1911); previous record: 90°F (2/12/1996).

10 2004 (10–11): An Alberta clipper's 50 mph winds blew 1" new snow/snow on the ground into drifts up to 20' high in northwest ND; some "whiteout" conditions. The eastbound Amtrak Empire Builder backed up 15 miles to Williston when stopped by a drift 12 to 14' high and 400 yards long.

11 1999: Today's snowfall of 57" at Tahtsa Lake West, BC, set Canada's 24-hour snow record, smashing the old record of 46.5" (1/17/1974) at Lakelse, BC (which replaced the previous record set, amazingly, on 6/29/1963, at Livingston Ranger Station, Alberta).

12 1950: Seeking shelter from a tornado by going into a ditch (or other low-lying area) should be an option of last resort. Near Sligo, LA, a pedestrian died when a car rolled into the ditch into which he had sought shelter.

13 2001 (11–13): Snow in CA's Death Valley National Park? The biggest snowstorm in many a memory of spotters and law enforcement officials left 2 to 3+' snow in some higher elevation sites. 36–42" at Towne Pass (el. 4,956') and Father Crawley Point (el. 4,000').

14 2006: An avalanche near Pass Fork of Rainy Pass of the Alaska Range swept a snowmobiler to his death; he was buried under 30' of snow. Several snowmobilers were breaking trail through heavy snows that had fallen on part of the Iditarod Sled Dog Race route.

15 2000: Amarillo, TX, set unusual temperature records today. The high of 82°F smashed the old daily high of 76°F set in 1921, and the morning low of 41°F broke the old high low record for the date of 40°F (also set in 1921).

16 2001: A car often is a poor place of shelter from a tornado; it can be lifted, rolled, bounced, crumpled, etc. A lady abandoned her car for a ditch as a tornado approached MS's Holmes County State Park; the car was blown on top of her; she died.

17 2006: A safety rule for driving in dense fog: do not stop on a freeway or heavily traveled road unless absolutely necessary. Because of fog, a truck stopped on I-295 near Jacksonville, FL; a 20-vehicle chain reaction accident resulted. One person killed; 7 injured.

18 1991: Freezing rain caused a number of traffic accidents, shutting down I-81 between Marathon and Polkville, NY. After reopening, the interstate was shut down again in only 7 minutes due to additional accidents.

19 1991: Not a tornado, just a severe thunderstorm. Winds to 100 mph and hail to 1.5" diameter pounded Floresville, TX. A 2.5-ton truck was reported to have been "pushed" ¼ mile into a field. Some children were cut by glass shards when hail broke bedroom windows.

20 1985: Lightning hurt a large tree, formed a fireball, and rolled into a house in St. George, KS. Phones started ringing all over town. The lightning strike was so bright that students at a school 2 blocks away thought the lights had been turned on and off.

21 2005: Hail (to 2.75" diameter) pummeled Canton, GA. Canton's public works department had to clear roads of ice; some streets lined by hail 15 hours after the storm. Three large car dealerships had entire inventory damaged ($3 million). 100 cars parked at a Walmart damaged.

22 1997: Rare (for the location) wintertime lightning at Oxford, NH. One bolt hit a tree and traveled to an underground cable, which exploded. A ditch 75' long and up to 4' deep resulted in the frozen ground. A different bolt struck another tree, killing a chained dog.

23 1997: Although terrain enhanced annual rainfall can pass 400" in parts of HI, most coastal sites receive only 25 to 30". Honolulu received 2.18" in 24 hours ending at 8 P.M., about 1/10 of its average annual amount.

24 2001: In a house without a basement, an interior bathroom offers a good place of safety from most tornadoes. A two-story house near Greenwood, MS, was destroyed by an F3 tornado. A family of 4 survived in the first floor bathroom, the only part of the house not destroyed.

25 1994: 5 to 8" snow fell on southern third of lower MI; winds to 35 mph; near zero visibility. Accidents closed parts of I-94, I-96, I-75, and US-131 for hours. Near Grand Rapids, a car hit a moving train; the driver said she did not see the train crossing in front of her.

26 2004 (26–27): Snow thunderstorms produced snowfall rates of 2 to 3"per hour in parts of NC's piedmont into upstate SC. Snow 12 to 22" deep common from southern part of metro Charlotte, NC, to Rock Hill, SC; some roofs collapse.

27 2003: The 2nd heavy snow in a week led to a 14-vehicle pile-up on I-40 in Flagstaff, AZ. In the pile were four 18-wheelers and an 8,000-gallon gasoline tanker. Fortunately, no ignition occurred. However, traffic backed up for several miles and I-40 was closed for 5 hours.

28 1902: Spring flooding from Buffalo River and Cazenovia Creek in S Buffalo, NY, was characterized by waters filled with floating ice and wrecked outhouses, wooden sidewalks, boxes, and barrels. Several families were rescued from the second floors of their houses.

29 2000: This "Leap Day" brought record warmth to WI. The 59°F high at Wausau is its highest February temperature on record. Calendar-day highs were set at Rhinelander (58°F), Green Bay and Oshkosh (59°F), Madison (60°F), and Milwaukee (61°F).

MARCH

1 1910: The deadliest avalanche in U.S. history swept engines and carriage cars from 2 snowbound trains (on a grade leading to Stevens Pass, WA) into a canyon. Fatality estimates range from 96 to 118. The Wellington Station house was also swept away.

2 1960: An ice storm, worst in memory, knocked down hundreds of miles of power and telephone lines in northern Alabama; adjacent parts of northern Georgia covered by 1 to 4" ice. 90 percent of trees in Alabama's Dekalb County damaged. Ice stayed on the ground in some places until March 11th.

3 1985 (1–4): A major winter storm left about 80% of South Dakota's roads blocked from late today to the evening of the 5th, 10 to 20" of snow general; 33" at Milbank and Summit; drifts to 20'. Power poles/lines downed due to ice in extreme southeast.

4 1841: President William Henry Harrison took his oath of office on a chilly (48°F), cloudy, windy day. His speech took 100 minutes; he rode a horse to and from the Capitol without a hat or overcoat. He caught a cold, which went to pneumonia, and he died one month later.

5 2004: Strong gradient winds (to 59 mph) caused much damage in central Illinois; several semis blown over. In Paris, an SUV driver died when a falling tree limb smashed through the roof of her car. A Champaign, IL city bus was blown off a bridge and fell 15' into a creek; 6 hurt.

6 2005: An avalanche near Colorado's Aspen Highlands Ski Area killed a man involved in an avalanche awareness class. While skiing across a slope, he fell, rolled, and triggered the avalanche, which carried him almost all the way down the mountainside.

7 1960: Dust devils are not just a western U.S. phenomenon. A dust devil in Sudbury, MA, ripped a small plane from its moorings, sent it flying 40' through the air, and smashed it against a fence.

8 1990: Near Ward, AR, 41 students and their driver were stranded in their school bus in water 4' deep; flooding had washed out bridges. After 2½ hours, they were rescued without any problems.

9 1998: Good thing this morning's F1 tornado, which destroyed 20 amusement park rides, along with bleachers and outbuildings, did not hit the St. Lucie County Fairgrounds (near Fort Pierce, FL) when the fair was in session. $3.2 million damage.

10 1986: Near Livermore, KY, during a severe thunderstorm, a 58-year-old man tried to hold a barn roof down with a chain. The winds of the storm prevailed; the roof was blown off and the man was thrown 78' in the air. He died of chest and head injuries.

11 1956 (10–11): Winds to 80 mph in southern lower MI caused much damage. Blizzard conditions in northern MI; snowdrifts 6 to 8' common. Many northern communities isolated 1 to 2 days. Snow in the north accompanied by lightning and thunder, somewhat unusual for this time of year.

12 1993 (12–13): "Storm of the century" mauled Florida—tornadoes, hail, wind, snow (to 4" north of Pensacola to near Crestview) and an unprecedented winter storm surge along the Gulf Coast (to 12' in Taylor County; 10 deaths). 25 direct deaths, $1.6 billion damage.

13 1993 (12–13): The worst winter storm in Alabama history left snow over the entire state; 12 to 20" Birmingham to northeast corner of state; 2 to 4" common along the Gulf Coast. Frequent lightning at times gave the atmosphere an "eerie blue-tinged glow." 400,000 homes without power.

14 1990: Talk about a quick reaction. Near Halley, AR, a couple heard a loud "pop" during stormy weather. They immediately went into a nearby closet for shelter. Good thing, because an F1 tornado destroyed three-quarters of their house. They were uninjured.

15 1998: A "rogue" wave swept out of the Pacific Ocean into the harbor parking lot at Port Arena, CA. Thirty cars were displaced and much sand and debris as well as many logs were deposited in the lot.

16 1965: Severe storms wracked parts of OK's Grant and Kay counties. Scattered heavy hail fell for 5 to 20 minutes along most of the path. At Nash, hail ranged in size from ¾ to 2" (ground covered to 2" deep), with some fist-sized clusters containing 5 stones each.

17 1894: With today's 80°F high in Sioux Falls, SD (a record for the date, and until 3/7/2000, the earliest 80°F on record), one might have thought winter was leaving. But –4°F record lows on the 25th will show the fickleness of Great Plains weather.

18 1925: The Tri-State tornado became the deadliest (695 killed; 234 at Murphysboro, IL) and longest (219-mile continuous path from near Ellington, MO, to northeast of Princeton, IN) tornado in U.S. history. 66 school deaths—including 33 at Desoto, IL (U.S. record).

19 1963: At Becks Mill, IN, 2 women died when their shelter from a tornado collapsed on them. The fruit cellar (behind the house) may have been weakened by rain; the house suffered only broken windows. One of the women had been hurt by an F3 tornado on 4/3/1956.

20 2003: In Georgia, there's seldom enough snow to get out of school, but flooding, now that is something else. Early A.M. rain closed 30 roads (washed out 10) in Laurens County. County schools let out early because of extensive flooding and road closures countywide.

21 1932: Alabama's deadliest single tornado (an F4) killed 49 people on its 60-mph path from north of Marion to the northwest corner of Coosa County. Entire families were killed, and 150 families were left "destitute." four other tornadoes killed 30 or more the state.

22 1897: Two teachers and a number of students of Arlington (GA) Academy stood at windows observing a storm. Suddenly, an F2 tornado destroyed most of the building. At least 8 of the school's 29 students died.

23 1990: High winds and high lake levels caused an ice breakup on Lake Champlain. Wind-driven blocks of ice caused much damage to docks, boats, and lakefront cottages on NY's and VT's shorelines. Locals said the unusually clear ice made it especially destructive.

24 1990: Dime-sized hail fell on Union City, OK, during a thunderstorm. Not unusual, except the temperature at Union City was almost freezing. In fact, the same storm also produced sleet and freezing rain.

25 2000: Near Shelter Cove, CA, a rogue wave swept a lady with a Canadian school group into the ocean. Four members of the group tried to rescue her, but were overcome by waves and currents. Two of the rescuers were rescued by a fishing vessel and the Coast Guard.

26 1999: South winds to 50 mph roared most of the day across central/north-central SD. Blowing dust blocked out the sun and reduced visibilities to near zero at times. In Selby, part of a hotel's 2nd- and 3rd-floor front wall was blown off by the wind.

27 1961: Wind gusts across Illinois, often 50 to 80 mph; 2 killed, 19 injured. A 100 mph gust toppled wind equipment from roof of the FAA station at Joliet, IL. A man died when blown off a steel beam at Streator Township High School; a Mason City TV repairman hurt when blown off a roof.

28 1956 (27–28): Gusty winds to 80 mph damaged $1.5 million acres in eastern Colorado; pilots noted dust to 20,000' above ground. Dust closed roads east of Limon due to near zero visibility. Schools at Arriba, Bennett, Stratton closed due to dust and wind.

29 1992 (28–29): Heavy rains falling on a deep snowpack caused ice-jam flooding at Blanchard, ME (Piscataquis County). Chunks of ice 50" thick and 10 to 15' across moved a barn 75 yd. Tractors and pickup trucks also found new resting places thanks to the force of the ice.

30 1998: Severe thunderstorms and heavy rains raked southeast Wisconsin today. At Lakeland College (near Johnson), the campus wastewater treatment buildings were flooded and sewage backup problems ensued. Classes were cancelled the next day.

31 1959: Hail to 11.5" in circumference dug holes in the ground south of Thackerville, OK; the stones also came through the roofs and broke neon signs. At Shawnee, large hail knocked a 17-year-old boy unconscious.

APRIL

1 1978: In Latrobe, PA, a gust of wind picked up an elderly man and hurled him into the sidewalk; he was killed. Winds at the Latrobe airport were measured at 85 mph.

2 1956: As a tornado passed through parts of Wilmette, IL, in the early morning, its barometric pressure reductions resulted in "rear windows of cars blown out" and "sealed beam headlights popped out of their receptacles."

3 1956: Severe storms (wind, rain, hail, and a few tornadoes) swept across much of IL. At Joliet, peak winds gusted to 109 mph before the anemometer was destroyed. In Chicago, 9 people were injured when they were blown through a barricade and into an excavation.

4 1968: Would homeowner's insurance have covered this? Winds to 50 mph pushed Lake Champlain ice up and over embankments at Tabor's Point (West Swanton, VT). Ice piles to 30' high approached/threatened 10 houses. In one case, the ice finally stopped 10' from a house.

5 1951: 120 people were lying on the floor of the Bridge Creek School near Blanchard, OK, when it was unroofed and its top part destroyed by today's F2 storm. Only 2 injuries. Better luck than on 5/3/1999 when 12 people were killed in Bridge Creek area by an F5 tornado.

6 1999: The chimney of the Mother Irene Gill Library (College of New Rochelle in New Rochelle, NY) was hit by lightning. Stone/concrete crashed into the hall below, occupied by 20 faculty/students. They escaped uninjured.

7 1988: 60+ mph winds caused a dust storm that deposited salt on power lines in southeast Idaho; rain dissolved the dust. Chemical reactions ignited material in the insulators, thus causing many power pole fires. Power outages ensued for 7,000+ customers.

8 1998: Lightning hit a tree and shed at Bellevue, WA. It knocked a hole in the roof of the shed and caused 2 bags of lawn chemicals stored in the shed to explode.

9 1991: A squall line of severe thunderstorms (gusts generally to 60+ mph; some to 110 mph) raced across WV; serious damage in 49 of 55 WV counties. two deaths, 86 injured, $16 million damage. Some rural counties had nearly all roads blocked by fallen trees.

10 1997 (10–11): 6 to 14" rain fell on TX's Lavaca County. A van washed off a road between Yoakum and Sweet Home; 2 couples followed a fence line to a tree. They clung to the tree for 2 hours, having to endure both rising water and fire ants. They survived both ordeals.

11 1956 (10–11): A dust storm raged across Oregon into southeast Washington before rain falling through the dust caused a "brown rain." A muddy mess coated sidewalks/buildings/cars. Driving impossible at times—as wipers could not remove mud.

12 1934 (11–12): Today's 121 mph gust atop Mt. Washington, NH (el. 6,288'), became the world's highest recorded surface wind. A 5-minute wind speed of 188 mph was also recorded today. The 24-hour average was 128 mph.

13 1987: In Memphis, TN, a man was struck by lightning while pumping gas into his car. Several hours earlier, 2 men were hit by lightning while working on a parked aircraft at the International Airport. Fortunately, all 3 survived.

14 1988: Lightning struck a tree near a home in Moab, UT, and came into the house on the underground phone lines. A 13-year-old girl talking on the phone was seriously burned. She was lucky; several people are killed in the U.S. each year in similar circumstances.

15 1982: The earliest-in-the-year tornado of record in ND was on the ground for 6 miles near Lisbon. The F2 storm was up to 440 yards wide. It destroyed a barn, uprooted trees, and drove tree branches through steel granaries.

16 2003: Just 1 lightning bolt. It hit an ONCOR transmission line near Granbury, TX, and resulted in 4 power plants temporarily shutting down. Up to 400,000 customers were without power for up to 2 hours.

17 1994: In Fort Fairfield, ME, 3'-thick chunks of ice littered lawns due to earlier flooding of the icy Aroostock River.

18 1950: A small house was thrown 200 yards into another home by an F2 tornado near Mobile, AL. As the storm passed near the University of South Alabama campus, a seismograph recorded a 73-second-long vibration produced by the passing tornado.

19 1968: A devastating hailstorm (stones to 2.5" diameter) raked the Long and Short communities in OK's Sequoyah County. Southeast of Short, hail stripped bark off the windward side of cedar trees. Cattle were "literally beaten to death" by the hail.

20 1896: For some readers, 100+ year-old descriptions may be a bit hard to visualize. An F4 tornado killed 2 (in a totally flattened home) and hurt 20 at Booktown, OH. The tornado "crept along the ground like a mammoth rock" and "smoke puffed at the top like an engine."

21 1951: An F4 tornado tracked 30 miles from near Lebanon to near Soso, MS. Two people died when a house was leveled. A body was found 200 yards from the site, and a refrigerator 300 yards from the home.

22 2001: A lightning bolt struck a house in Sioux Falls, SD, and injured a person standing in the basement. Strange, but here's why: the basement was "wet," so the charge of the bolt was able to find a pathway via the moisture to the victim.

23 2001 (22–23): Extreme changes. Pierre, SD, set its heaviest snow of record for so late in the season (12.5"). By the 28th, the snow was melted and a record date high (96') was set. On only one earlier date in the year has Pierre seen a high =96°F. 90°F on 1/21/1900.

24 2002: Near Popular Bluff, MO, a woman took shelter from an F4 tornado in her bathtub. Both were blown 200' into the median of US-67. She survived. A big chunk of asphalt from the same highway was blown through the window of a car, hurting a person inside.

25 1910: An incredible day in the southeast part of the U.S. with a trace of snow noted as far south as Pensacola, FL. In Nashville, TN, today's 1.5"-snow was its April 24-hour record, and its latest measurable snow. Today's 32°F was also Nashville's latest freeze of record.

26 1998: To increase the odds of surviving a tornado in a home without a basement, seek shelter on the ground floor, in a small interior room, like a closet. Two people were unhurt when their home near Hale Center, TX, was destroyed by an F2 tornado—by doing just that.

27 1968: Lightning hit a pine tree near a house in Enon, MS. It ran underground, then entered the house, destroyed part of the living room, and sent wood splinters flying. A woman sitting in a corner had 2 splinters embedded in her temple, but was not seriously hurt.

28 1950: The power of violent tornadoes. An F4 tornado near Clyde, TX, blew a small refrigerator more than ½ mile and "lodged" it atop a telephone pole. Near Holdenville, OK, a couple was found (dead) in the wreckage of their home, which had been blown 150 yards.

29 1968: A dust devil with a loud "jet plane" roar damaged trailers, carports, and TV antennas in Pepperell, MA; plywood sheets "sailed away." In Franklin, a dust devil ("2 telephone poles high" and with a loud whistling noise) lifted a 500 lb. boat into a tree.

30 1898: A violent F4 tornado struck near Hospers, IA, as a father was about to go into the outside storm cellar; he had a young child under each arm. The home was annihilated. The children were found dead, still in their father's arms.

MAY

1 1929: "Lightning does not strike twice" and "tornadoes do not hit the same location twice" are both myths. The city pump house at Fort Smith, AR, was damaged by a tornado today. On 12/17/1929, it will be destroyed by another tornado.

2 1990 (2–3): Record and near-record late heavy snow fell on southeast CO and northeast NM. 18.6" near Kim, CO; 18 to 22" in NM in Des Moines/Capulin/Folsom area. In NM's Union and Colfax counties 1800 newborn calves ($1 million value) died of hypothermia and exhaustion.

3 1984: Flying debris is a potential hazard of severe thunderstorm winds. A fiberglass bench was blown off the 21st floor of Peachtree Summit Building in downtown Atlanta, GA. Unfortunately, the bench landed on a car on I-75/85, killing a backseat passenger.

4 1963: Hail size often references local features. Hail to "hedge apple" size left the ground white in parts of Coffey/Franklin counties (KS). A few larger conglomerate stones near Burlington, Sharpe, and Waverly had a 4.5" diameter and 14" circumference.

5 1998: An F1 tornado made a brief 3-mile track at Los Altos, CA. During its brief lifetime, it picked up and hurled (and injured) a tennis coach about 20' at Los Altos High School.

6 1983: 60 mph wind gusts caused dust storms (most dust from plowed fields in central IL) in northern IL; visibility near zero at times. Many accidents, including a 9-car/2 semi-trailer incident on I-57 near Rantoul. Chicago's skyline was nearly invisible from a short distance away.

7 2004: Thunderstorm winds to 83 mph overturned a number of portable toilets near the re-enactment main stage at VA's Battle of Spotsylvania. 3 Amtrak trains were stalled near Chatham by downed trees/power lines.

8 1998: Not a tornado, but the winds were stronger than most tornadic wind speeds. Downburst winds to 120 mph caused $1.5 million damage in Kingsport, TN. 100 businesses and 70 homes damaged; roofs blown off and windows blown out. Many trees and power lines downed.

9 1980: A blinding squall, then near zero visibility in fog at the Sunshine Skyway Bridge over FL's Tampa Bay. A ship hit a bridge piling, causing a 1,200' section to collapse into the bay. Several vehicles, including a bus, drove over the edge of the span; 35 deaths.

10 2000 (4–31): A prescribed burn (4th) in NM's Bandilier National Monument became a firestorm today that swept into W Los Alamos and the National Laboratory; µ250 homes/buildings wrecked. 48,000 acres burned; 21,000 people evacuated. $1.5 billion property damage.

11 1963: Not typical of fire damage found in most parts of the country. Prairie fires started by lightning and rapidly spread by strong winds burned 5,000 acres of grass in W Clark County (KS); 4 miles of fence posts destroyed at one ranch.

12 2004 (11–12): A very late-season snow/ice storm hit north-central/northeast ND. Snows 8 to 12" toppled 150 power poles in Mountrail County. High winds/ice to 1" diameter downed 750 power poles, mainly east of ND-1 from Fairdale to Canadian border.

13 2002 (12–13): Flash flooding occurred on almost every watercourse in MO's Iron County; $5.5 million damage. Many people trapped in cars by floodwater. Near Ironton, a man crossing Stouts Creek by foot to rescue his dogs was swept away or drowned.

14 1956: A few miles N of Martinsville, VA, on VA-108, thunderstorm winds tore off part of a truck's tailgate. Unfortunately, it smashed through the windshield of another car, killing the 2 women inside.

15 1834 (12–16): A wintry period from the Great Lakes to parts of New England. 6" snow at Erie, PA (14); 12" at Rutland, VT, by P.M. today. Newbury, VT, received 2' (sleighs on roads on 16th), and the Haverhill, NH, vicinity had 2' in valleys and 3' on hills.

16 1962: At the wrong place at the wrong time. 6" rain in 45 minutes caused a wall of water 6' high, which swept a pickup off a highway near Clarendon, TX; the 2 occupants drowned. The truck was swept 100' from the highway; 1 body was carried 5 miles.

17 1962: Near Pecos, TX, thunderstorm winds picked up 8" x 16" cinder blocks, blowing 1 through a car window, and others through cinder block walls. In Pecos, falling hailstones (to 3" diameter) "looked like huge snowballs" and bounced 5 to 10' upon hitting the ground.

18 1997: A thunderstorm downburst (gust to 81 mph) hit the Parkersburg, WV, airport; windows broken in 14 vehicles. The tower was briefly evacuated. The weather observer said, "We thought we were having hail, but it wasn't hail. It was busted glass flying around."

19 1973 (18–19): Parts of central NY received their heaviest, latest snow of record; 10" at Old Forge, 8" at Waterville, 6" at Boonville and Oneonta. Many trees and power lines down due to heavy, wet snow. Some schools closed.

20 1963: Thunderstorms killed 4 people in ME. A fishing boat on Bowler Pond (Palermo) was capsized by high winds; its occupant drowned. A plane crashed at Bath, killing the 3 occupants. The crash was attributed to either turbulence or a lightning strike.

21 2004: Hail to 3" deep (drifts to 10") caused a car on I-94 east of Glendive, MT, to skid off the road and blow a tire; nobody hurt. South of Glendive, a flash flood washed out a hole 10 to12' wide by 15 to 20' deep on a gravel road. Fortunately, nobody drove into it.

22 1951 (21–22): 12" rain led to disastrous flooding (6 deaths) at Hayes, KS; water to 20' deep in parts of town. 75 city blocks and Fort Hayes State College campus inundated. Now I-70 travelers are probably unaware of a flash flood potential as they race past Hayes.

23 1960: Sea waves and accompanying tidal action from Chilean earthquakes affected AK's Gulf of Alaska coast from Prince of Wales Island to Montague Island for up to a week beginning today. Today's 2 tidal waves near Yakutat were up to 14' high.

24 1951: Northeast gales caused waves to 15' high in the harbor at Newport, RI. A 50' Navy launch with about 142 men on board capsized; 19 of the men drowned in the incident.

25 1956: Dust devils swirled over eastern MA. A child and bicycle at Ipswich were tossed 40'; at Dudley, a child and tricycle were tossed 10'; both children were injured. One of the dust devils was said to be preceded by a sound "like the baritone siren of a freight train."

26 1978 (26–27): 10" rain fell in 90 minutes just west of Canyon, TX. Flash flooding destroyed 15 houses, 27 mobile homes, 300 vehicles, and 12 camping trailers as far downstream as Palo Duro Canyon State Park (swept by a 12' high wall of water). Four killed, 15 injured.

27 1963: Dense fog and vehicles traveling at high speeds make a deadly mix. At 3 A.M., a number of vehicles drove into a fog bank covering part of the NJ Turnpike at Elizabeth. Five drivers and 1 passenger killed; 10 injured.

28 1990: As the beach patrol warned people (thousands present) to get out of the water and off the beach at W end of TX's Galveston Island, a woman was struck and killed by lightning as she attempted to get her children out of the water.

29 1959: A man fled his car and jumped into a ditch east of Washington, KS, as a tornado approached. The car was picked up and blown over him; he grabbed the rear bumper but was unable to hold onto it. Lucky for him: the biggest piece of his Rambler found was 3' x 7'.

30 2001: At Prichard, AL, while sitting on a barber's chair and talking on the phone, a man was hurt by a lightning strike. Knocked unconscious, he awoke 45 minutes later in the hospital. Other than soreness, he had no apparent serious injuries.

31 2002: A searing end to May brought record May monthly heat to Safford, AZ (109°F); McCook, NE (106°F); Goodland, KS (104°F); and Rifle, CO (99°F). The 102°F May record high in Delta, UT, followed Delta's all-time May low of 19°F set on the 9th.

JUNE

1 1956: Not good to be close to 5,000 lb. of dynamite when it explodes. Lightning "prematurely" exploded that much dynamite at a MA turnpike construction site near Woronoco. 25 men were within 300' of the blast epicenter. five were hurt; amazingly, no deaths.

2 1993: A Little League baseball game in North Salt Lake, UT, was interrupted by a tornado. Players and spectators took shelter just before the tornado hit. Many people covered with mud/debris; 2 hurt from flying debris. Windows blown out of several vehicles.

3 1860: A massive tornado swept an 80-mile path from east Cedar County (IA) to near Whiteside, IL; 92 killed (41 in Comanche, IA). 23 killed on a raft as the tornado crossed the Mississippi River; 3 survivors ended on the IL shore with no memory of how they got there.

4 1956: Dust devils caused problems in Benson, AZ, several times this month. Today, a large dust devil damaged a number of roofs in town, and demolished a small house and carport. On the 26th, a dust devil collapsed the rear wall of an unoccupied church.

5 1960: Fifteen milk cows were found dead, lying in a circle around a small apple tree near Pownal, VT. Lightning killed them, although the tree exhibited no lightning damage.

6 2002: The parking lot of a closed service station at Somers Point, NJ, was hit by lightning; it traveled to the underground storage tank. The resulting explosion left a crater 50' in diameter and 8 to 10' deep.

7 1946: Only 5 people have been killed by tornadoes in MT since 1880. An F3 tornado near Froid destroyed a 5-room farmhouse; furniture was blown over 1 mile. One fatality was due to a falling chimney.

8 1960: "Chunks" of hail up to the size of hen eggs fell for 45 minutes at Hooker, OK; rain to almost 4" accompanied the storm. Much property and crop damage.

9 2005: Tropical Storm Arlene formed at 0600 UTC (2 A.M. EDT) about 175 miles west/southwest of Grand Cayman and became the 1st of what would be a record 27 named storms for the 2005 Atlantic hurricane season. Landfall west of Pensacola, FL, on the 11th with 60 mph sustained winds.

10 2005: Unlike Hurricane Katrina, which would cause 1300+ deaths in the U.S., Tropical Storm Arlene caused very little damage and 1 death. The fatality occurred when a Russian exchange student was caught in a rip current off Miami Beach, FL, produced by Arlene's winds.

11 1965: Heavy rains fell on an unusually deep snowpack in the high Uintas of UT. After midnight, a flash flood roared down Sheep Creek Canyon, destroying 3 recreation areas, 7 bridges, and 5 miles of newly paved roads. 7 swept away while sleeping at Palisades Campground.

12 1993: A tornado that started as a waterspout over the Missouri River and destroyed a house moved onshore near Pierre, SD. The owner hid in the fireplace and survived. He was lucky, because falling chimney stone has been the cause of a number of deaths.

13 1973: At Jennison, MI, a dust devil picked up a rug, stepladder, and a patio umbrella. It also lifted a 350-lb. concrete patio table and dropped it 3' away (in several pieces after the landing).

14 1998: Iowa's 24-hour rainfall record set at Atlantic, IA, with 13.18"; resultant flooding destroyed 21 homes. Saturated soil around Lake Panorama began sliding into the lake; 3 homes "cracked" beyond repair as earth sank 12 to 18".

15 1992: A legendary storm for chasers: ≥12 tornadoes in 3 hours in Mitchell County, KS. A farmer south of Cawker City reported new tornado damage to his farm each of 5 times he went to, and than came out of, his basement. One time he noted 3 on the ground and 4 in the air.

16 1998: Today's 103°F in Midland, TX, was the 1st of 14 days in a row the high was ≥100°F. The old record: 12 days (July 14–25, 1981; June 30–July 11, 1964). This June was the second warmest of record, behind June 1990.

17 1992: Weather sometimes has no respect for majesty. Severe thunderstorm winds blew down IL's largest tree, which was also the largest eastern cottonwood in the U.S. The tree, 138' tall, was in Gebhard Woods State Park.

18 2002 (17–18): Deadly floods ravaged parts of southern Russia between the Caspian and Black seas; Chechnya, Krasnodar, and Stavropol particularly hard hit. 40,000+ homes flooded and 200+ bridges damaged or destroyed. 100+ deaths.

19 1992: Midday severe thunderstorms produced $600 million damage to Wichita and south-central KS. At least 70 people treated for minor injuries, mainly due to hail and hail-broken glass. 377,000 acres of crops damaged/destroyed.

20 1988: At Raleigh, NC, an employee of a fast-food restaurant was injured by a lightning bolt while serving food from the drive-up window.

21 2006: The National Weather Service Forecast Office in Birmingham, AL, reported thunderstorm winds blew over 2 portapotties at the intersection of AL-49/AL-14 in Tallapoosa County. Apparently, they were not in use at the time as no injuries were reported.

22 2006: Thunderstorm outflow winds 50 to 70 mph raked US-62/82 in northeast Terry County (TX). Near zero visibility in blinding dust and sand led to multiple accidents; 15 injured. An elderly man died when he drove into a tow truck assisting at an accident.

23 2001: Neither snow nor rain nor heat nor gloom of night stays these couriers from the swift completion of their appointed rounds. How about lightning? It hurt a mailman ready to check a mailbox in Venice, FL. Rain started; his arm hair stood up just before he was hit.

24 1979: Too bad this tornado was not videotaped. Forming near the east side of CO's Pikes Peak, an F2 tornado moved down Williams Canyon into Manitou Springs. Convenience store and gas station demolished; several homes severely damaged. One person hurt.

25 1950: A Northwest Airlines DC-4 flying at 3,500' in an area of thunderstorms crashed into Lake Michigan about 20 mi. from Benton Harbor; all 58 on board died. No official cause for crash, but weather suspected.

26 1989: Near Junction City, KS, a woman was struck by lightning when she got out of her car to film an approaching storm. The bolt hit the top of her head, killing her instantly.

27 2004: A number of people took shelter from an approaching storm by standing under trees lining a parkway connecting a parking lot to a beach at GA's Buford Dam State Park. Lightning strikes hit a tree(s) and killed 3 people instantly; 6 others hurt.

28 2005: Tropical Storm Bret formed <50 miles east/southeast of Veracruz, Mexico. Combined with Arlene, this June became the 13th time since 1851 that 2 June tropical storms formed. Landfall on the 29th near Tuxpan; flooding in state of Veracruz killed at least 1.

29 1989: An F1 tornado near LaCenter, WA, lifted a car 6' into the air and turned it around 180° before setting it back down. The driver was slightly cut and bruised (and probably a bit surprised). Several trees were also blown down by this 15-yard-wide tornado.

30 1972: Lightning struck and killed a 23-year-old man as he was walking through Bay-Brook Park in Baltimore, MD. A witness said the man "flew through the air and seemed to explode." His clothes were ripped off; some pieces of clothing were found 80' away.

231

JULY

1 1997: 4" of rain fell in 90 minutes on a 4-square-mile area neat Pitcairn, PA; led to flash flooding. Water from Dirty Camp Run flowed through the elementary school's lower-level windows. 13 buildings swept off their foundations. $10 million damage.

2 1977: Occurring during one of the worst drought seasons in CA history, showers generated by an unusual July occluded frontal passage left .35" rain on San Francisco (CA) International Airport. This is the highest daily July rainfall on record for the airport.

3 1995: On Lake Shawnee (KS), as a woman was pulling an inner tube connected by a rope into a boat, lightning hit water nearby. She was electrocuted; 3 other people in the boat were unhurt.

4 2002: Lightning struck a vendor display area just east of the tunnel entrance to the infield of FL's Daytona Beach International Speedway. Six people were treated and released at the scene; 2 others were hospitalized.

5 1966: It would have made an interesting video segment in a television sportscast. Near Anoka, MN, a tornado "chased" 30 people from an archery range. Fortunately, they ran south and the tornado veered north.

6 2002: The Chediski-Rodeo Complex fire was contained in AZ's Navajo County. The merger of 2 human-caused wildfires (begun in June), 468,638 acres burned, as did 426 structures/homes. 30,000 people evacuated. Flame heights to 300 to 400' noted during some uphill runs.

7 2000: A farmer's worst nightmare. Hail to ⅞" diameter caused a swath of destruction in a 2-mile-wide, 20-mile-long path from west of River Falls to north of Hager City, WI. $4.5 million damage to corn, soybeans, alfalfa, and small greens. 21 square miles a total loss.

8 2000: Rash flooding occurred in Chapman Gulch near Ophir, CO, trapping a motorist who had driven through the gulch moments earlier with water up to the hood of the vehicle. The motorist was able to leave the morning of the 9th after the waters receded.

9 1995: Electrocutions have resulted from similar events. At Bristol, FL, lightning hit a tree, traveled into a nearby septic tank, and followed the piping into the bathroom toilet of a nearby house. A man sitting on the "throne" went airborne, but did survive.

10 1982: A rare event for AK: 2 funnel clouds were observed 10 miles northeast of North Pole, AK. They lasted about 5 minutes and reached to within 500' of the ground.

11 1951 (10–11): Snow fell at some locations in the northern Rocky Mountains and, incredibly, in the Black Hills. On the 10th, 6. 5" reported at the E entrance of WY's Yellowstone NP and 2" at Mystic Lake, MT. On the 11th: Lakeview, MT, 2", and Bixby Dam, SD, 0.4".

12 2001: A nearly stationary supercell thunderstorm dropped large hail and 3 to 6" rain in 1 hour southeast of Cohagen, MT; hail drifts to 10' deep were measured in coulees. Four days later, golf-ball-sized hail was still embedded in mud/straw, along with drifts to 4' deep.

13 2004: Driven by 60 mph winds, 2.75"-diameter hail damaged most buildings/vehicles in Posen, MI. Holes punched in siding and roofs. 300 holes in a church roof; a greenhouse lost 1,000 2' x 2' windowpanes. One man's back badly bruised as he moved his vehicle to shelter.

14 1987: Ball lightning hit a home in NY's Oneida County, went through the house, down the stairs to the cellar, into an oil furnace, through a repairman, and into the ground. He collapsed but survived. When he got home, it was without power due to lightning.

15 2000: Lightning is a major danger to hikers in the CO Rockies in summer. Near Conundrum Hot Springs (Pitkin County), a bolt struck 1 of a group of 4 hikers. Her clothing was shredded and boots blown off. Injuries included bleeding from nose and ears; burns on chest and feet.

16 2005: Hurricane Emily briefly a Category 5 hurricane 100 miles southwest of Jamaica; lowest pressure was 929 mb/highest sustained winds 160 mph. Emily is the only known July Category 5 hurricane of record in the Atlantic basin, and the earliest Category 5 on record.

17 2000: Intense storms produced a vivid lightning display in the early morning over Kansas City, KS/MO. 2,000 plus cloud-to-ground bolts hit Johnson County between 2 and 3 A.M.; the number of intra-cloud bolts may have exceeded 20,000 in the same time span.

18 1910: A chilly morning in the Ozark Mountain valleys of AR. In fact, this morning's low of 41°F in Harrison set the state's all-time record low for July.

19 1956: 70 tourists were at the bottom of CO's Royal Gorge enjoying the view. A 10' high wall of water from a cloudburst over Telephone Gulch roared into the gorge and knocked a small girl off the platform. A tourist managed to grab her and kept her from being swept away.

20 1998: Heavy rain from severe thunderstorms in Las Vegas, NV, combined with a clogged drainage system to cause the roof of the Palace Station Hotel and Casino to collapse. The same structure caught fire when hit by lightning several hours later.

21 1985: Near Blanding, UT, 2 women were running to their truck. One of them was jumping over a ditch just as lightning struck; she was knocked unconscious, but survived. The other died of cardiac arrest.

22 2002: Heavy rain and hail caused a land/rock slide, which covered CR-306 (Cottonwood Creek drainage near Buena Vista, CO) with debris to 10' deep/1-mile long. An elderly couple's van was swept off the road; mud/rocks flowed into it. They suffered hypothermia, cuts, and bruises.

23 2005: An Atlantic hurricane hitting southern CA? Sort of. Remnants of former Hurricane Emily (tropical moisture transported west/northwest), in the form of early A.M. thunderstorms, awoke many people from the deserts to the coast of CA's San Diego County.

24 1999: Today's high of 97°F a record for NYC, NY's Central Park (4 daily records and 1 tie by month's end; 101°F on 5th and 6th were daily records and hottest this month). This month had an average daily temperature of 81.4°F, eclipsing 1955's record 80.9°F.

25 2004: Rain to 9" caused an 18' high wall of water, which raced down Dry Creek 25 miles north/northeast of Dryden, TJC 100'-long pavement slabs of TX-349 washed away; mud/gravel to 4' high topped other highway areas. 13 workers were trapped 36 hours at a well site encircled by water.

26 1995: A prime rule for lightning safety is not to seek shelter under trees or other tall objects. Nonetheless, 9 campers at Camp Tuscaror, a Boy Scout Camp in NY's eastern Broome County, were injured when struck by lightning as they stood under tall pines.

27 1987: An F3 tornado tracked 30 miles in a general southwest direction (most travel NE) from near Red Wing, MN, to north of Fairbault. It leveled 2 farms in Welsh Township; debris/equipment was blown hundreds of yards. A horse was seen flying "horizontally" through the air.

28 1996: Only 15 to 20 yards wide, an F1 tornado blew out all windows on the south side of a house near Mercer, ND, as it passed within 20 yards. A pickup was moved 7', and the family car was picked up and spun around 180°. Shingles tom off house roof; $75,000 damage.

29 1997: A lightning safety rule is to stay away from windows. At Aspen Park, CO, a woman received minor injuries when she was struck by lightning after it passed through an office window. She was temporarily blinded for 15 minutes.

30 2001: At 12:30 P.M. CDT, thunderstorm downburst winds to 86 mph damaged buildings at the airport, bent a flagpole, and knocked down trees and power poles at Wagner, SD. An accompanying heat burst raised the temperature 20°F (to 99°F) in a few minutes.

31 1969: At Sanford, MI, a couple tried to hold the roof onto their patio when the wind threatened to remove it. As the roof did start to lift, the man let go. The wife held on and was carried over the house and landed 75' away. She died.

AUGUST

1 2002: A 76-year-old man was found dead in his uncooled apartment at De Soto, LA. According to the coroner, the apartment had air conditioning, but the man was not using it in order to save money to buy medication for his diabetic/coronary conditions.

2 2002: Thunderstorm wind gusts to 83+ mph toppled thousands of trees, power lines, and poles in NJ's Monmouth County; 168,000 homes/businesses without power. 250-year-old trees to 8' diameter downed. $1.5 million damage to Monmouth University; its offices closed 5 days.

3 1990: A record heat wave smothered England and Wales; the high of 99°F at Cheltenham the highest-ever temperature on record for the UK (until 101°F at Brogdale on 8/10/2003). At Liverpool (England) the entire stock of a chocolate factory melted.

4 1992: Thunderstorm microburst winds to 100 mph caused more than $500,000 damage to a farm at East Georgia, VT; several cows had to be killed. In 1907, a barn on the same farm was destroyed by thunderstorm winds; 42 cows died.

5 2002: Some good luck and timing for the crew. Near Glenwood Springs, CO, a freight train was halted by 4 to 5' of mud left by a flash flood. As the crew scrutinized the situation, another flash flood deposited several feet of mud and debris on the tracks behind them.

6 1961: Thunderstorm winds to 100 mph raked parts of Lake Texhoma, boundary between OK and TX. 100+ boats were sunk or damaged; similar destruction to piers. One drowned when a boat was capsized by the storm.

7 1979: Seiches (sudden changes in water levels) noted at Lake Ontario shore locations in Rochester, NY, vicinity; rises to 3' followed by falls and rises of several feet within a few minutes. Severe thunderstorms were over west Lake Ontario at the time.

8 2004: An alia (fishing boat) was upended by a huge wave near the beach at Fogagogo (American Samoa), causing the engine to fall off. The alia's 4 fishermen were not seriously hurt. High swells were caused by strong high pressure far to the south.

9 2002: Vehicles are not always safe refuges from hailstorms. Wind-driven hail (to 1.5" diameter) broke windows of a pickup near Hertick, SD; a man sitting inside the truck was injured by high-velocity hail. Hail in the area accumulated to 6" deep, drifts to 2' deep.

10 1973 (10–12): Forest fires and avalanches can lead to potential landslide problems when heavy rains fall on the denuded slopes. Heavy rains led to mudslides, which covered 2 miles of Thane Road (Juneau, AK, area) at the site of a snowslide on January 22nd this year.

11 2004: If your car is stalled in high water, look for downed power lines before exiting the vehicle. At College Point, NY (NYC metro area), 2 people were electrocuted by a fallen power line when they left the car and stepped into water several feet deep.

12 1972: In Mississippi's Sunflower County (near Ruleville), lightning struck and killed 1 of 2 boys walking down a turnrow. The county coroner said the 2nd boy was not seriously hurt, "the lightning just knocked him down and he jumped up and ran."

13 2002: A heatburst hit San Angelo, TX, just before midnight. Downdrafts from dying thunderstorms warmed the temperature from 75°F at 11:35 P.M. CST to 94°F at 12:05 A.M.; humidity fell from 62 to 19%; wind gusts to 40 mph. By 12:30 A.M., readings back to 73°F and 66%.

14 1946: Southern U.S. has no concern with freezes this time of year; not so with southern AK. Today's 32°F low at Anchorage became its earliest autumn freeze on record. Its all-time record high: 86°F on 6/25/1953.

15 1958: Fortunately, most tornadoes are relatively weak. A cooperative weather observer's pickup truck was lifted 20' and dropped upright by a tornado in a forested part of Easton, CT. He noted a swirling mass of limbs/debris some 100' above ground.

16 1972: A neutercane (term retired in 1973; subtropical cyclone is now used) deepened offshore Crescent City, CA, and made landfall near Brookings, OR. Winds 70 mph sank at least 10 boats, damaged 100. 13 drowned (4 in CA waters, 9 in OR waters).

17 1969: Hurricane Camille (only 1 other modern-day storm a Category 5 at U.S. landfall) moved inland west of Pass Christian, MS, with winds to 200 mph and a 24.6' storm surge. Total destruction in some coastal areas near eye. 144 plus Gulf Coast deaths.

18 1972: At Kapoho Vacationland (on the Puna Coast, Island of Hawaii), waves to 30' high (generated by Tropical Storm Diana) swept 4 homes from their foundations. Waves knocked down a couple and swept them into bushes, but did not pull them out to sea.

19 1972: Hurricane Celeste passed 25 miles northeast of Johnson Island, an atoll 1 square mile in size with highest point <20' above sea level; winds more than 100 mph. The civilian and military population of 500 was evacuated (18th) due to the danger of stored toxic gases escaping.

20 1999: A waterspout from the Atlantic Ocean moved onshore as an F2 tornado at Beach Haven, NJ; $4.2 million damage. The Sea Spray Motel was severely damaged (sprayed with more than sea water); its 150 vacationers were displaced.

21 2003: August is summer in the northern Hemisphere but winter in the southern Hemisphere. This was likely the coldest August night on record for South Africa as new monthly records were established throughout the country. Johannesburg's 19°F set its new record.

22 2002: Thunderstorm winds to 80+ mph tore a 100'-long blimp from its berth at Timmerman Field (Milwaukee, WI); it flew 6 blocks before impacting 4 homes. Windblown rain came through Miller Field's retractable roof—saturating the baseball field and some spectators.

23 1999: Video games provide excitement, but this may have crossed the line. At Sanford, ME, a man playing a video game in the American Legion building was injured when a lightning strike arced through all the video machines. He suffered chest pains and hearing problems.

24 2005: Tropical Storm Katrina formed in the central Bahamas. Katrina would become the costliest weather disaster in U.S. history: damage estimates more than $100 billion. Flooding of New Orleans, LA, would displace more than 250,000 people, more than displaced in the 1930s' Dust Bowl.

25 2005: Hurricane Katrina made its 1st U.S. landfall on FL's east coast between Hallandale Beach and North Miami Beach; sustained winds of 80 mph, gusts of 90+ mph. Katrina killed 14 as it crossed extreme southern FL, including several killed by falling trees and tree branches.

26 1999: 2 to 6" rain pounded the NYC metro area; mass transit crippled during the morning rush. Water 3 to 5' deep at some subway stations; part of the N-bound platform of the 6 line at 28th Street washed away. Some parkways closed; trains with thousands of riders stranded.

27 1999: Moisture from remnants of Hurricane Bret ignited thunderstorms that raked west side of Phoenix, AZ. Microburst wind/rain led to the evacuation of several thousand people from the Desert Sky Mall; parts of the roof collapsed 10 minutes after the evacuations.

28 2005: Hurricane Katrina's peak intensity of 175 mph sustained winds occurred about 225 miles south/southeast of the mouth of the Mississippi River. The 4 P.M. National Hurricane Center bulletin warned of Gulf Coast storm surges to 28' and "Some levees in the Greater New Orleans Area could be overtopped."

29 2005: Hurricane Katrina made its 2nd U.S. landfall just south of Buras, LA, as a Category 3 storm; sustained winds 125+ mph. New Orleans Lake Front Airport reported sustained winds of 69 mph, gusts to 86 mph. The LA/MS death toll (mostly surge/flooding) was more than 1,300.

30 1979 (8/25–9/7): Hurricane David's lowest pressure (924 mb) and highest sustained winds (173 mph) were south of Puerto Rico today. 60,000 of the island of Dominica's 80,000 residents were left homeless by David's direct hit (29th); 56 deaths there.

31 1954: Winds to 86 mph from Hurricane Carol felled the steeple atop Boston's (MA) Old North Church (in which lanterns were hung to tell Paul Revere the British were coming). The steeple was built in 1806 to replace the original steeple toppled by an 1804 hurricane.

SEPTEMBER

1 1979: In the Houston (TX) Ship Channel the oil tanker Chevron Hawaii was hit by lightning from storms of Tropical Storm Elana; 3 killed, 4 injured in ensuing explosion/fire. Oily rain covered lawns/houses downwind (from smoke combining with raindrops).

2 1974: At about 1:30 A.M., a weak tornado skipped across parts of the Bronx and Mount Vernon, NY. The path width varied between 50 and 200 yd.; its length was 2 miles. It caused minor damage and no injuries.

3 1997: Thanks to 4.5" rain, a 12' high wall of water washed over AZ-14 and the Red Rock-Randsburg Road near Cantil, AZ; 4 cars were swept away, but no deaths; 100 motorists stranded. Much flooding in Red Rock Canyon State Park. $5 million damage; 4 injuries.

4 2004: Astronomical summer can be anything but "warm" in the high Rockies. A hiker froze to death on the summit of CO's Longs Peak, as a not rare snowstorm with high winds swept the area. A hooded sweatshirt, jeans, and tennis shoes were his only cold weather gear.

5 1933: A hurricane made landfall just north of Brownsville, TX. A wind gage blew away at 106 mph; estimates to 130 mph. Drifted citrus blocked roads; reports of houses floated 10 miles by surge. Some farmland within 10 miles of bay still unproductive due to salty surge.

6 1997: Lightning can strike any time of the day. A Saturday morning football game was marred at 8:35 A.M. in Fruita, CO, when lightning hit 2 power poles at a middle school. Several cheerleaders were knocked to the ground by the shock wave.

7 2000: Lightning hit near a basketball hoop at Oceanside (CA) High School as 200 students met for PE class. Two knocked unconscious said it was as if hit by a rock or needles through their skin and hair pulled. 100 students "jolted"; hair on arms and heads stood on end; 3 injuries.

8 1900 (8–9): America's worst natural disaster (number of deaths) occurred when a hurricane with 120 mph winds and a 20' storm surge killed 6,000 in Galveston, TX. 1,200 died elsewhere. Following the storm, the surf was 300' inland from the former waterline.

9 2004: Close call for 17 campers near Conneaut Creek in OH's Ashtabula Counry. Rain (nearly 5") caused a rapid rise in water and put a campground under 5' of water shortly after midnight. The campers barely escaped the water's rise and had to be rescued by boat.

10 2004: A wall of water and mud to 10' high raced down CA's Borrego Palm Canyon and into Borrego Springs; a campground (fortuitously empty) was obliterated. 70 to 90 homes were damaged in Borrego Springs by mud to 2' deep. $1 million damage.

11 1998: 2" rain fell on parts of UT's Zion National Park in 24 hr. Flow in the Virgin River at the park headquarters went from 280 to 4,200 cfs in 4 hr. The raging water created a sinkhole 30' long by 15' wide by 20' deep in the Zion Canyon Scenic Drive.

12 1976 (11–12): Japan's 24-hour rainfall record of 44.80" at Hiso (Tokushima Prefecture) was caused by Typhoon Fran. Fran was also responsible for 167 deaths in Japan.

13 2000: A hurricane hazard sometimes not in mind. Hurricane Florence, far beyond the horizon, nonetheless generated large swells that caused rip currents along NC beaches. Two people drowned an hour apart at Kure Beach, and another at Carolina Beach.

14 1974: A flash flood roared down NV's El Dorado Canyon into Nelson's Landing. A trailer park (35 house trailers), bar, restaurant, 50 vehicles, and part of a boat landing were washed into Lake Mojave. Nine deaths.

15 2004 (13–16): Hurricane Ivan affected coastal AL/W FL Panhandle; landfall occurred near Gulf Shores, AL, early on 16th. A buoy just south of the AL coastal waters reported an incredible peak wave height of 52' today before breaking loose of its mooring.

16 2004: Hurricane Ivan made landfall near Gulf Shores, AL, early morning. Some deaths after the storm's end: a 7-year-old boy killed by a falling limb while he watched a tree being removed; an 83-year-old man fell off a damaged roof he was repairing.

17 2004 (16–17): 90,000 apple trees were blown down by remnants of Ivan in NC's Henderson County. On 16th, a debris flow of water/trees/boulders/mud from the top of Fishhawk Mt. destroyed/damaged 20 to 30 homes/mobile homes in Peeks Creek Valley; 4 died near Macon.

18 2004: WY's Wind River Basin lived up to at least part of its name. A wild fire just south of Riverton, spread by 30 to 35 mph southwestern winds, burned 300 acres, 33 vehicles on a used car lot, 4 campers, and a mobile home used for storage; 9 injured; $1 million damage.

19 2000: Sure looked like a western wildfire, with trees and houses burning and some flames shooting skyward more than 50' high. But instead, the wildfire was just north of Oklahoma City, OK (from 9 miles south to 3 miles south of Guthrie); 35 homes destroyed.

20 1962: Near Fruitland, NM, lightning hit the tin chimney of a hogan during a native ceremony; 2 killed, 2 injured. Yesterday, at Missoula, MT, "dry" lightning (meaning little, if any, rain was produced by the storm) burned a grain elevator; 50,000 bushels of wheat ruined.

21 1962: Amazing what lightning can do when it hits a person, yet not cause death. At McCammon, ID, the zipper fastener on a schoolboy's jacket and trousers were fused by a lightning strike. He did suffer severe burns.

22 1995 (21–22): Some things are out of a farmer's control. Record early cold and freezing temperatures covered most of IA overnight; as cold as 24°F this morning in Emmetsburg and Sibley. 30 million bushels of soybeans lost, along with some corn. $204 million crop loss.

23 1997 (23–25): Surf as high as 20' pounded HI's north beaches; the surf was generated by what had been Typhoon David in the north Pacific. 30+ surfers, bodyboarders, and swimmers were rescued along Oahu's Sunset Beach and Waimea Bay.

24 2001: 10 trailers on the campus of the U of MD were destroyed by an F3 tornado. One occupant was thrown into a nearby dumpster; others "dug their hands into the carpet" and held on for dear life as the tornado pulled their feet up in the air.

25 1997: Add El Niño in the east Pacific, large swells from a distant storm in the Gulf of AK, effects of Hurricane Nora, and high tide. The result: 5 to 8" waves moving onshore and flooding a 14 block stretch of Seal Beach, CA. Quick response by the city crews limited damage.

26 2004: Thunderstorm rains closed part of TX-118 with water to 6' deep between Fort Davis and Fort Davis State Park. Two campers were trapped in Short Canyon for almost 24 hour. They were rescued by helicopter on 27th at a deserted ranch house near Wild Rose Pass.

27 1962 (27–28): Gale-force winds/heavy rains pounded ME. Tides to 4' above normal; falling trees downed many power and phone lines. At Fort Fairfax, a close call: Strong winds blew a boy and the canopy on which he was lying from a moving truck; no serious injuries.

28 1962: Seattle, WA's, 1st known tornado (a waterspout over Lake Washington) caused mainly minor damage in small areas of the northeast part of the city. However, a house roof was severely damaged in the View Ridge area, as was a hangar roof at Sand Point Naval Air Base.

29 2004: Although Hurricanes Charley (in August) and Frances/Ivan/Leanne (in September) had exited FL, their effects were long lasting. According to the Insurance Information Institute, 1 of every 5 houses in FL received damage from 1 or more of these storms.

30 1875: What whether observers "observe" has changed with time. Among the remarks noted by the Lynchburg, VA, observer, was today's migration of hundreds of squirrels across the James River.

234

OCTOBER

1 1986: All it took was an estimated 5 seconds for thunderstorm winds of 75 mph to lift two aircraft at TN's Tullahoma Airport, and then dash them into the ground upside down. One was totally destroyed. Two hangars were also damaged.

2 1858: Wind, rain, and damage accounts show the only known tropical system to hit southern CA as a hurricane produced Category 1 winds at San Diego and tropical storm force winds at Long Beach. A similar storm in 2007 might produce $200 million damage in the same area.

3 1964: Hurricane Hilda produced an F4 tornado, which tracked west/northwest 2 miles through LA's Lafourche Parish. 22 people killed in Larose; debris blown 16 miles to the west. 38 people killed by Hilda; 22 by this tornado.

4 1777: Dense fog cloaked the battle of Germantown (PA). Smoke from the fight combined with fog to make it "almost as dark as night." Due in part to the poor visibility, Americans at times shot each other, helping the British eventually win the battle.

5 2004: Baseball-sized hail pounded Socorro, NM, for 5 to 10 minutes. The result was $40 million damage in Socorro County, of which $15 million occurred on the New Mexico Tech campus. Nearly every university building was damaged, and the university vehicle fleet was almost a total loss.

6 1981: A Fokker F-28 aircraft flew into thunderstorms near Moerdijk, Holland. The detachment of its starboard wing led to a crash with the loss of all occupants. The plane had likely flown into a funnel just after the tornado lifted from the ground.

7 1997: Did he take his job home with him? At Mesa, AZ, hail accumulated to 6" deep. An employee of the National Weather Service reported roof tiles and a glass window were broken on his house.

8 1972: Between Guam and Rota in the Pacific Ocean, Typhoon Marie killed 2 men. Three men assumed dead were found 47 days later, 1,310 miles southwest of Guam by a Japanese fishing boat. In good health, they survived by eating fish and wringing rainwater from their clothes.

9 2005 (7–9): Remains of Tropical Storm Tammy helped dump 7 to 12+" rain on parts of NC's Robeson/Brunswick/New Hanover Counties. Much home and business flooding; many roads impassable; $2.5 million damage. Basement of Cape Fear Museum (46,000 artifacts stored) completely flooded.

10 1990: A 50' section of Kendall Lake Dam burst just upstream of Camden, SC. Motorists trying to push cars through waist-deep water were swept 50 to 100 yards downstream by the additional torrent; some held onto trees until rescued; 4 deaths in 1 stalled car.

11 2005: Ex-Hurricane Vince weakened to a tropical depression at 0000 UTC 155 miles west and southwest of Faro, Portugal. It passed just south of Faro and made landfall near Huelva, Spain. It is the only known tropical cyclone to reach the Iberian Peninsula. No casualties/serious damage.

12 1886: Landfalling hurricane between Sabine Pass, TX, and Johnson's Bayou, LA. Tidal waves said to be as high as 2-story buildings; surge extended 20 miles inland. 150 killed; survivors clung to trees and floated on mattresses. Two of 100 homes in Sabine Pass repairable.

13 1991 (13–14): A deep low-moving storm on the east side of the Kenai Peninsula helped give Anchorage, AK, its October record 24-hour snow of 11.6" (old record: 10" on 10/10/1940).

14 1966: Late-season severe thunderstorms brought up to softball-sized hail to parts of Brown, Dodge, Freeborn, Pipestone, Ramsey, Rock, and Steele counties in MN. A hailstone reportedly 16" circumference (MN record if true) smashed a truck windshield near Claremont.

15 1996: Waterspouts are not always confined to warm, tropical waters. Convective showers, which developed in a cold, unstable air mass, produced a waterspout over the Pacific Ocean off Seaside, OR. No damage occurred.

16 1984: An F1 tornado (25 yards wide with a 1-mile-long path) struck Lawler, IA, significantly damaging 4 homes. One resident said, "There was so much suction . . . we couldn't get the door to the basement open."

17 2005: Tropical Storm Wilma formed 0600 UTC 170 miles southeast of Grand Cayman. By 19th, Wilma explosively deepened to become the most powerful Atlantic hurricane of record with a pressure of 882 mb (26.05") and sustained winds of 185 mph 340 miles southeast of Cozumel, Mexico.

18 2004: A good day not to have been fishing. An F1 tornado near Higdon, MO, picked up a fishing boat from a pond, carried it 100 yards and dropped it in some trees. The tornado also wrapped a trampoline around a tree and left up to 2" of leaves inside a damaged home.

19 1992: Driving blind/driving too fast for the conditions? Dense fog (visibility often less than ¼ mile) led to a 30-car and 1 18-wheeler chain reaction accident on CA's I-15 near Rancho Cucamonga; 24 injuries. Road closed for more than 10 hours.

20 1991 (20–22): Strong northeast Diablo winds fanned a small brush fire into an inferno that destroyed more than 3,300 homes in the hills of Oakland and Berkeley, CA; 25 died and 150 were injured. Property damage exceeded $1 billion.

21 2003 (21–29): The Roblar 2 fire was started on the Camp Pendleton Marine Corps Base (CA) by live ammunition training; 8,592 acres burned before containment. Firefighters (more than 1,300) had to watch for unusual hazards—unexploded ammunition.

22 1996: Kansas City (MO/KS) whitened by a general 6–9" snow, its earliest and heaviest of record. The 6.1" observed at the International Airport became the official October single snowfall record for the city. Much tree and power line damage (175,000 people without power).

23 1997: An F1 tornado rolled a mobile home near Jasper, TX, 100 yards up a hill before it hit a tree. Two people inside were not seriously hurt because they had taken shelter in the bathtub shortly before the tornado hit the trailer.

24 2001: Fortuitous timing. An F1 tornado destroyed 4 classrooms and heavily damaged 8 others at the Davisburg (MI) Elementary School. The tornado hit 8:10 P.M. EDT.

The only other significant damage caused by the storm was some uprooted trees.

25 1997: Another good reason for having a smoke detector in your home! About 9:30 P.M., near Hartselle, AL, lightning struck a switchbox, traveled into the house, and set the house on fire. A man inside the house died of smoke inhalation.

26 1992: 2 men working at a rock quarry near Cookson, OK, were attaching caps to 24 sticks of dynamite when a bolt of lightning struck about ¼ mi. away. The resultant ground currents ignited the dynamite; the men died.

27 1959: The ship Mary Barbara reported a 958 mb pressure and estimated winds to 161 mph just outside Manzanillo (Mexico) Harbor. This "Manzanillo" hurricane was one of Mexico's worst; 1,000 deaths in and around Mammillo, Minatitlan, and surrounding areas.

28 1999 (28–29): Northwest swells caused high surf on CA's central/southern beaches. 40' high waves broke through the seawall at Capitola; some streets and businesses flooded. A 25' wave swept a honeymooning couple to sea (29th) from Lover's Point Beach (Pacific Grove); 1 killed.

29 1956: With a prolonged and deafening noise, an F3 tornado destroyed and damaged buildings west of Dorrance, KS; most were rebuilt after a 1951 storm. Near Hunter, a farmhouse was "utterly demolished." A mother and baby were blown 60' into a field, but had only bruises and scratches.

30 1993: Snow began very late (29th) over southwest IN and spread into southwest OH and west and north KY. Evansville, IN, whitened by a 24-hour October record 4.0". Today's 5.9" at the Cincinnati/N KY Airport set its October record and gave Cincinnati its first "white" Halloween.

31 1965: A major windstorm plagued the west half of NY and adjacent Great Lakes; wind gusts were to 80 mph near the Great Lakes and 60 mph inland. The St. Lawrence Seaway was closed for 11 hours, delaying ferry traffic between the U.S. and Canada.

NOVEMBER

1 2002 (10/29–11/4): Frigid temperatures followed the passage of an Arctic cold front across WA on October 29th. About 3.9 million bushels of apples were killed by the cold in Yakima Valley (lows to 4°F); $65 million loss to farmers.

2 1967: The Last Chance Motel in Emery, UT, was destroyed by a cone-shaped F2 tornado; furniture and bedding were thrown hundreds of yards. The tornado occurred at the unusual time (for a tornado) of 8:30 A.M. No injuries from this event.

3 2004: Winds to 65 mph blew down a number of trees in OR's Crater Lake National Park. Falling trees damaged the community center, the Good-by picnic area comfort station, a house in Sleepy Hollow, and part of the Science and Learning Center.

4 1988: A tornado touched down briefly near a school in McComb, MS. The tornado missed a filled football stadium by only 300 yards.

5 2002: Wind gusts to 70 mph at high tide led to $1 million damage to the Larsen Bay dock area on west side of AK's Kodiak Island. A tidal surge of 1 to 2' on top of the high tide caused waves that "smashed" the dock and pier and mess hall/bunkhouse floors from below.

6 1953 (6–7): Earliest, heaviest snow of record for much of the East Coast. Some records: 11.9" at Wilmington, DE; 6.5" at Washington, DC; 3.7" at NYC, NY. Greatest storm amount was 27.5" at Middleburg, PA. Many roads in central eastern PA closed by 3 to 4' drifts.

7 1998: Snowboarding and skiing can be risky fun. Five snowboarders were swept down a rocky slope of UT's Little Cottonwood Canyon of the Wasatch Mountains; 1 killed, 1 injured. Nearby resorts had not opened and avalanche controls had yet to be exercised.

8 1996: Tornadoes are relatively rare in PA; November tornadoes even more so. Nonetheless, an F1 tornado, with numerous, brief touchdowns, tracked 10 miles from near Kunkletown to near Syndersville. A house roof was blown 100 yards. Fortunately, no injuries.

9 2001: A wildfire spontaneously combusted in a 4-acre stump pit (50' deep) near Marshalls Creek, PA. Windy, dry weather combined with fallen leaves to spread the fire. Dense smoke led to potential respiratory problems for nearby residents. Fire put out on 12th.

10 2002: F0/F1 tornadoes are "weak" tornadoes; they are responsible for only 5% of tornado deaths, although they comprise 70% of all tornadoes. As an F1 tornado traveled through Crawford, MS, it killed a man as he attempted to warn neighbors of the approaching storm.

11 1987 (11–12): Heavy snow (to 17") whitened Washington, DC, and adjacent areas of VA/MD. Some motorists spent the night in their vehicles on I-295 or on the Woodrow Wilson Bridge; some students spent the night in their Prince George's College (MD) school.

12 1956: The icebreaker USS *Glacier* saw what may have been the world's largest iceberg. Seen about 150 miles west of Antarctica's Scott Island, the iceberg was about 60 miles wide by 208 miles long, or roughly the size of MD. (Date approximate.)

13 1992: The Peace Bridge between Buffalo, NY, and Fort Erie, ON (Canada), shut 7 hours when high winds toppled 2 semi-trailer trucks crossing the span over the Niagara River. The same winds caused Lake Erie levels to rise 3' in 1 hour on its eastern side; much flooding.

14 2001 (13–14): Smoke from a brush fire that started on the 11th in NJ's Pennsville Township became trapped under an inversion. Thick smoke caused schools to close, and closed several major roads in the A.M.

15 2001: An F0 tornado traveled 2 miles just northeast of Austin, TX; trees destroyed/carports and mobile homes damaged. A school in its potential path was having a tornado drill. With students in hallways, no further action needed. The tornado lifted before hitting the school.

16 2001: After several days of rain, dense fog developed in low-lying areas of south-central/southeast WI. The driver of a vehicle was killed when it struck a horse standing on WI-78 near Mazomanie; visibility was 10'. Sixteen children hurt when a Monticello school bus was hit by a truck.

17 2002 (16–17): A major ice storm glazed northern CT with up to ¾" ice; $2.5 million damage, mainly from falling trees. Towns such as Granby, Simsbury, and Canton without power for up to 5 days. 50 mph winds on 18th blew down trees and power lines still coated in ice.

18 1995: Winds to at least 89 mph caused much damage in central MT. Vehicles were blown off roads near Moore, Sunburst, Hays, and Brady. Roofs were damaged and many signs blown over.

19 1986: Early season snow records for parts of southeastern New England: 11" at Blue Hill Observatory (Milton, MA) beat the previous record of 8"; 4.2" at Providence, RI, set its early record. Even 1" fell on Cape Cod, MA. Storm on November 11 to 12, 1987, will establish new early records.

20 2001: Today's 31°F low is the latest 1st fall freeze on record for Albuquerque, NM (airport records began in 1931). An astonishing 80 of 91 fall lows (meteorological fall is Sept. through Nov.) were normal for Albuquerque.

21 2004: An avalanche hit 3 ice-climbers in First Gully near Eureka, CO. The lead climber fell 200' and was buried under 6" of debris; his back was broken. A second climber was partially buried up to his waist in a sitting position. All survived.

22 1993: Reduced visibility due to blowing snow, along with snow and ice, caused a 90-car pileup on I-90 in Spokane, WA, just before 11 A.M. 45 injuries; $500,000 damage. I-90 was closed for up to 5 hours.

23 2001: An F2 tornado passed from near Hunt to Salus in AR; 1 person killed in a mobile home. North of Hunt, 2 people were injured in 1 of 6 chicken houses destroyed at the location; 3 of the chicken houses destroyed contained 120,000 chickens; most perished.

24 1940 (23–25): Said to be worst ice storm in U.S. history through 1940, freezing rain and drizzle fell on north TX Panhandle. Ice on power lines to 6" circumference; weight of 13 lb/linear ft downed 1,000s of poles/trees. All power lost in Amarillo/Canyon for 3 days.

25 1985: Tornadoes are much rarer in South America than in North America. Today's tornado in Argentina's east Buenos Aires province tracked 25 miles; its width was up to 325 yards wide. It produced a lot of damage at Dolores, where 1 person was killed.

26 1995 (26–27): Heavy snow closed I-70 between Eisenhower Tunnel and Vail Pass, CO for several hours, stranding hundreds of travelers going home from ski resorts at the end of Thanksgiving weekend. The American Red Cross opened many temporary shelters.

27 1997: A windy day in NYC, NY, for the Macy's Thanksgiving Day Parade. The strong winds (50 mph gusts) led to balloon handlers losing control of the Cat in the Hat balloon. It hit the top of a light pole, which fell on 4 onlookers; all hurt, 1 seriously.

28 1912 (27–28): Snowfall is a rare event in FL. The record earliest snowfall for FL (and its only November snow) fell during the night across parts of the interior counties in the far northwest (Madison to Gadsen) bordering GA. Up to ½" was reported at Mt. Pleasant.

29 2001: Flash flooding widespread across central/north-central TN; a number of roads were closed. The only wooden bridge left in Stewart County was washed away. Many schools closed because of flooded roads.

30 1997: Based on medical reports, at Milwaukee, WI, an 88-year-old woman found dead on her driveway died of hypothermia. Low temperatures were in the mid-high 30s. It is speculated she fell down and was unable to get up.

236

DECEMBER

1 2004: Winds to 50 mph caused trees and wires to topple in Bath, NY. A 10' high facade of a building was blown down, falling on a woman 15' below. Her rescuer was injured by continuing debris fall.

2 1982: Today became Chicago's warmest winter day on record with a high of 71°F and a low of 58°F.

3 1973 (3–4): An ice storm in extreme southeast New England toppled 1,000 poles, uprooted trees, and cut power to 25 towns (worst damage southeast of a line from Superior to Plattsmouth). Some rural areas without power for 4 to 6 days.

4 1973: In the Braman area of IN, a tornado "only 5–10' wide and 50' high" damaged a garage, overturned a boat and trailer, and threw a pontoon boat into trees. A truck on US-6 was lifted from the roadway and slammed into a tree; 1 injury.

5 1975: An F2 tornado hit the gym at Eastern Oklahoma State College in Wilburton, OK; 200 people were in the gym, but only 3 were hurt (by flying glass). Good luck continued as the tornado hit the west wing of a nursing home, but injured no occupants.

6 1997: Biggest rains in at least 70 years totaled 4 to 8" in CA's central Orange County; 10" at Mission Viejo. Hillsides collapsed; many mud/debris flows; much flooding. Areas such as Newport Bay's Rhine Channel so clogged they looked like landfills. $17.7 million damage.

7 1950: All American Airlines at Connellsville, PA, observed winds of 60 mph with gusts to 75 mph. At least 8 vehicles damaged by falling buildings. A boy was blown into a creek, but rescued.

8 1973: Near Kulani Honor Camp (off Stainback Highway on island of Hawaii), strong winds toppled an ohia tree on a hunter and pinned him; his companion was unable to lift the tree and went for help. The pinned hunter was killed by more falling trees before help arrived.

9 2003: Although a "fish" storm (it never threatened land), a subtropical storm became Tropical Storm Peter 700 mi. west/northwest of the Cape Verde Islands. This is the first time since 1887 that 2 tropical storms formed in the Atlantic Basin in December.

10 1995: In frigid pans of the U.S., motorists are advised to have cold weather survival gear in their vehicles. 30 mi. southeast of Ontonagon, MI, a man was found frozen to death in a snowbank near his disabled vehicle. Temperature was as low as –15°F, windchill to –60°F.

11 2002: An unusual event in NJ's Lafayette Township: a satellite dish repairman had to be rescued from the roof of a building after it iced over while he was working on the dish. Rain turned to ice on contact with the cold roof surface.

12 1995 (11–12): A Pacific storm raked OR; gusts: 119 mph (Florence), 112 mph (Cannon Beach), 101 mph (Astoria), 74 mph (Portland, downtown windows blown out). Falling trees killed 2; a livestock gate caught by the wind killed a woman opening it. $25 million damage.

13 1987 (12–14): Heavy snow and high winds raged across most of NM; much of the interstate system closed. Snow totals to 3' in higher elevations. Unofficial wind gust at Sandia Peak Tramway northeast of Albuquerque of 124 mph this P.M.; Coronado Airport wind gust of 107 mph.

14 2005: At 5:15 A.M. a dam failed; 1.3 billion gallons of water raced through MO's Johnson's Shut-Ins State Park; most facilities destroyed or damaged. Park empty; in spring and summer often several thousand daily users. The annual dam break exercise is scheduled on this day.

15 2005: A major ice storm glazed much of the piedmont and adjacent mountain areas of GA, NC, and SC with up to ¾" accumulations. Many trees and power lines downed. 683,000 customers lost power. Fortunately, temperatures were not bitterly cold; mostly close to freezing.

16 1997 (15–16): Although Super Typhoon Paka left major damage to 60% of homes (1,160 single family homes destroyed) on Guam (wind gusts to 175 mph before instruments failed), 0 deaths and only 2 hurt. $500 million damage.

17 1973 (16–17): The worst ice storm in CTs history paralyzed central/western sections of state. Statewide tree damage was worse than damage caused by infamous 1938 hurricane. More than 250,000 homes were without power and heat for up to a week.

18 1971: Hail is unusual on the tropical islands of HI. Nonetheless, unusually large hail (for HI) the size of "marbles" and "half an inch in diameter and two inches long" was reported at Kealia (Kauai).

19 1978 (18–19): Unseasonably heavy rains of 1 to 3" on top of saturated ground and mountain snowpack led to record crests of NM's San Francisco, Gila, and Mimbres Rivers. The Gila, normally 5 to 6' wide at Redrock, was "nearly one mile wide" at crest this morning.

20 1977: Winds to 80 mph snapped a power pole on CA's Vandenberg Air Force Base; ensuing brush fire consumed 10,000 acres before brought under control. 450 plus firefighters; 30 bulldozers fought the fire. The base commander and 2 top base fire officials killed by the fire.

21 2002 (21–24): An unusual combination of rain and hail (hail is rare at low latitudes) caused flooding and landslides on Vanuatu's Tanna Island (southwestern Pacific); some bridges washed away. Many food gardens destroyed; 3,000 plus people affected.

22 1998 (21–25): Citrus/vegetables in CA's San Joaquin Valley seriously hurt by 5 nights of freezing temperatures. Today's 34°F high in Bakersfield its coldest-ever high, breaking the 35°F reading of 12/11/1932. Contrast this to today's record 32°F high in Battow, AK.

23 1973 (23–24): A blizzard played havoc with pre-Christmas travel in east CO; 11.8" at Denver's Stapleton Airport, where 10,000 people were stranded for 24 hours. Many roads blocked by drifts to 10' deep.

24 2001 (24–28): Almost no snow this season at Buffalo, NY, until this 5-day storm. 25.2' snow in 24 hours. (24–25): 4th largest on record; 35.4" in 24 hours (27–28): 2nd largest on record. 81.6" new storm total record; depth of 44' (28) record depth.

25 2001: Part of IN-257 in Pike County was barricaded due to flooding. At least 4 vehicles whose drivers ignored the barricades were swept away. One death likely late evening; vehicle found the 26th.

26 1996: An ice storm knocked out power to 269,000 people in WA's south Puget Sound region; Tacoma Narrows Bridge closed. Up to 10" snow in Seattle/Everett. 400+ flights canceled at Seatac Airport. Almost all hotels from Seatac to Tacoma full with stranded people.

27 2005: This December was OK's 4th driest (back to 1895). Wildfires burned 175,000 acres; 150 homes and businesses destroyed or damaged; $10+ million damage. Today's fires in Hughes County burned 10,000 acres. A 68-year-old male died while firefighting.

28 1978: Severe thunderstorms produced strong winds and golf-ball-sized hail in FL's northern Dade County. A 25-year-old jockey was struck and killed by a lightning bolt at Calder Race Course. He had just finished a race and was running for cover.

29 1973 (29–30): An F3 tornado ended its path at Fort Rucker, AL, causing only minor damage. The next day an F3 tornado caused $1 million damage to government buildings and a residential area in Fort Rucker, and injured 23 people.

30 2005: Tropical Storm Zeta became the 27th named storm of the 2005 Atlantic season, shattering the old record of 21 (1933). Although computer models kept advertising Zeta's demise, the storm managed to survive in the open waters of the central Atlantic through 1/6/06.

31 1968: Not a good way to end the year. Heat in an icehouse on MN's Lake Beebe was lost in cold, windy weather; wind chill down to –53°F. Three boys ice fishing suffered severe frostbite; 2 of them were in critical condition for a time.

GLOSSARY OF METEOROLOGICAL TERMS

ACCAS AltoCumulus CAStellanus; mid-level clouds (bases generally 8 to 15 thousand feet), of which at least a fraction of their upper parts show cumulus-type development. These clouds often are taller than they are wide, giving them a turret-shaped appearance. ACCAS clouds are a sign of instability aloft, and may precede the rapid development of thunderstorms.

Advection Transport of an atmospheric property by the wind.

Air-mass Thunderstorm Generally, a thunderstorm not associated with a front or other type of synoptic-scale forcing mechanism. Air-mass thunderstorms typically are associated with warm, humid air in the summer months; they develop during the afternoon in response to insolation, and dissipate rather quickly after sunset. They generally are less likely to be severe than other types of thunderstorms, but they still are capable of producing downbursts, brief heavy rain, and (in extreme cases) hail over ¾ inch in diameter.

Aurora It is created by the radiant energy emission from the sun and its interaction with the earth's upper atmosphere over the middle and high latitudes. It is seen as a bright display of constantly changing light near the magnetic poles of each hemisphere. In the Northern Hemisphere, it is known as the aurora borealis or northern lights, and in the Southern Hemisphere, this phenomena is called the aurora australis.

Barotropic System A weather system in which temperature and pressure surfaces are coincident, i.e., temperature is uniform (no temperature gradient) on a constant pressure surface. Barotropic systems are characterized by a lack of wind shear, and thus are generally unfavorable areas for severe thunderstorm development.

Blizzard A blizzard means that the following conditions are expected to prevail for a period of 3 hours or longer: Sustained wind or frequent gusts to 35 miles an hour or greater; and considerable falling and/or blowing snow (i.e., reducing visibility frequently to less than ¼ mile).

Cap (or Capping Inversion) A layer of relatively warm air aloft (usually several thousand feet above the ground) which suppresses or delays the development of thunderstorms. Air parcels rising into this layer become cooler than the surrounding air, which inhibits their ability to rise further. As such, the cap often prevents or delays thunderstorm development even in the presence of extreme instability. However if the cap is removed or weakened, then explosive thunderstorm development can occur.

The cap is an important ingredient in most severe thunderstorm episodes, as it serves to separate warm, moist air below and cooler, drier air above. With the cap in place, air below it can continue to warm and/or moisten, thus increasing the amount of potential instability. Or, air above it can cool, which also increases potential instability. But without a cap, either process (warming/moistening at low levels or cooling aloft) results in a faster release of available instability—often before instability levels become large enough to support severe weather development.

Cb Cumulonimbus cloud, characterized by strong vertical development in the form of mountains or huge towers topped at least partially by a smooth, flat, often fibrous anvil. Also known colloquially as a "thunderhead."

Cell Convection in the form of a single updraft, downdraft, or updraft/downdraft couplet, typically seen as a vertical dome or tower as in a towering cumulus cloud. A typical thunderstorm consists of several cells. The term "cell" also is used to describe the radar echo returned by an individual shower or thunderstorm. Such usage, although common, is technically incorrect.

Celsius Temperature Scale A temperature scale where water at sea level has a freezing point of 0°C (Celsius) and a boiling point of +100°C. More commonly used in areas that observe the metric system of measurement. Created by Anders Celsius in 1742. In 1948, the Ninth General Conference on Weights and Measures replaced "degree centigrade" with "degree Celsius." Related term: Centigrade

Cirrus One of the three basic cloud forms (the others are cumulus and stratus). It is also one of the three high cloud types. Cirrus are thin, wispy clouds composed of ice crystals and often appear as veil patches or strands. In the mid-latitudes, cloud bases are usually found between 20,000 to 30,000 feet, and it is the highest cloud that forms in the sky, except for the tops, or anvils, of cumulonimbus, which occasionally build to excessive heights.

Climatology The study of climate. It includes climatic data, the analysis of the causes of the differences in climate, and the application of climatic data to the solution of specific design or operational problems.

Cold-air Funnel A funnel cloud or (rarely) a small, relatively weak tornado that can develop from a small shower or thunderstorm when the air aloft is unusually cold (hence the name). They are much less violent than other types of tornadoes.

Confluence A pattern of wind flow in which air flows inward toward an axis oriented parallel to the general direction of flow. It is the opposite of difluence. Confluence is not the same as convergence. Winds often accelerate as they enter a confluent zone, resulting in speed divergence which offsets the (apparent) converging effect of the confluent flow.

Convection Generally, transport of heat and moisture by the movement of a fluid. In meteorology, the term is used specifically to describe vertical transport of heat and moisture, especially by updrafts and downdrafts in an unstable atmosphere. The terms "convection" and "thunderstorms" often are used interchangeably, although thunderstorms are only one form of convection. Cbs, towering cumulus clouds, and ACCAS clouds all are visible forms of convection. However, convection is not always made visible by clouds. Convection which occurs without cloud formation is called dry convection, while the visible convection processes referred to above are forms of moist convection.

Convergence A contraction of a vector field; the opposite of divergence. Convergence in a horizontal wind field indicates that more air is entering a given area than is leaving at that level. To compensate for the resulting "excess," vertical motion may result: upward forcing if convergence is at low levels, or downward forcing (subsidence) if convergence is at high levels. Upward forcing from low-level convergence increases the potential for thunderstorm development (when other factors, such as instability, are favorable). Compare with confluence.

Cumulus One of the three basic cloud forms (the others are cirrus and stratus). It is also one of the two low cloud types. A cloud that develops in a vertical direction from the base (bottom) up. They have flat bases and dome- or cauliflower-shaped upper surfaces. The base of the cloud is often no more than 3,000 feet above the ground, but the top often varies in height. Small, separate cumulus are associated with fair weather (cumulus humilis). With additional heating from the earth's surface, they can grow vertically throughout the day.

Divergence The expansion or spreading out of a vector field; usually said of horizontal winds. It is the opposite of convergence. Divergence at upper levels of the atmosphere enhances upward motion, and hence the potential for thunderstorm development (if other factors also are favorable).

Dust Bowl The term given to the area of the Great Plains including Texas, Oklahoma, Kansas, Colorado, and New Mexico that was most greatly affected during the Great Drought of the 1930s.

El Niño The cyclical warming of East Pacific Ocean sea water temperatures off the western coast of South America that can result in significant changes in weather patterns in the United States and elsewhere. This occurs when warm equatorial waters move in and displace the colder waters of the Humbolt Current, cutting off the upwelling process.

Flash Flood A flood which is caused by heavy or excessive rainfall in a short period of time, generally less than six hours. Also, at times a dam failure can cause a flash flood, depending on the type of dam and time period during which the break occurs.

Fahrenheit Temperature Scale A temperature scale where water at sea level has a freezing point of +32°F and a boiling point of +212°F. More commonly used in areas that observe the English system of measurement. Created in 1714 by Gabriel Daniel Fahrenheit (1696–1736), a German physicist, who also invented the alcohol and mercury thermometers.

Fog Fog is water droplets suspended in the air at the earth's surface. Fog is often hazardous when the visibility is reduced to ¼ mile or less.

Freeze A freeze is when the surface air temperature is expected to be 32°F or below over a widespread area for a climatologically significant period of time. Use of the term is usually restricted to advective situations or to occasions when wind or other conditions prevent frost. "Killing" may be used during the growing season when the temperature is expected to be low enough for a sufficient duration to kill all but the hardiest herbaceous crops.

Front A boundary or transition zone between two air masses of different density, and thus (usually) of different temperature. A moving front is named according to the advancing air mass, e.g., cold front if colder air is advancing.

Frost Frost describes the formation of thin ice crystals on the ground or other surfaces in the form of scales, needles, feathers, or fans. Frost develops under conditions similar to dew, except the temperatures of the earth's surface and earthbound objects fall below 32°F. As with the term "freeze," this condition is primarily significant during the growing season. If a frost period is sufficiently severe to end the growing season or delay its beginning, it is commonly referred to as a "killing frost." Because frost is primarily an event that occurs as the result of radiational cooling, it frequently occurs with a thermometer level temperature in the mid-30s.

Funnel Cloud A condensation funnel extending from the base of a towering cumulus or Cb, associated with a rotating column of air that is not in contact with the ground (and hence different from a tornado). A condensation funnel is a tornado, not a funnel cloud, if either a) it is in contact with the ground or b) a debris cloud or dust whirl is visible beneath it.

Green Flash A brilliant green coloration of the upper edge of the sun, occasionally seen as the sun's apparent disk is about to set below a clear horizon.

Greenhouse Effect The overall warming of the earth's lower atmosphere primarily due to carbon dioxide and water vapor, which permit the sun's rays to heat the earth, but then restrict some heat-energy from escaping back into space.

Ground Fog Fog created when radiational cooling at the earth's surface lowers the temperature of the air near the ground to or below its initial dew point. Primarily takes place at night or early morning.

Gulf Stream The warm, well-defined, swift, relatively narrow ocean current which exists off the east coast of the United States, beginning near Cape Hatteras. The term also applies to the oceanic system of currents that dominate the western and northern Atlantic Ocean.

High Wind Sustained wind speeds of 40 mph or greater lasting for one hour or longer, or winds of 58 mph or greater for any duration.

Humidity Generally, a measure of the water vapor content of the air. Popularly, it is used synonymously with relative humidity.

Ice Storm An ice storm is used to describe occasions when damaging accumulations of ice are expected during freezing rain situations. Significant accumulations of ice pull down trees and utility lines resulting in loss of power and communication. These accumulations of ice make walking and driving extremely dangerous. Significant ice accumulations are usually accumulations of ¼" or greater.

Inversion Generally, a departure from the usual increase or decrease in an atmospheric property with altitude. Specifically it almost always refers to a temperature inversion, i.e., an increase in temperature with height, or to the layer within which such an increase occurs.

Lake Effect Snow Snow showers that are created when cold dry air passes over a large warmer lake, such as one of the Great Lakes, and picks up moisture and heat.

Landspout [Slang] A tornado that does not arise from organized storm-scale rotation and therefore is not associated with a wall cloud (visually) or a mesocyclone (on radar). Landspouts typically are observed beneath Cbs or towering cumulus clouds (often as no more than a dust whirl), and essentially are the land-based equivalents of waterspouts.

Lenticular Cloud A cloud species which has elements resembling smooth lenses or almonds and is more or less isolated. These clouds are caused by a wave wind pattern created by the mountains. They are also indicative of downstream turbulence on the leeward side of a barrier.

Microburst A convective downdraft with an affected outflow area of less than 2½ miles wide and peak winds lasting less than 5 minutes. Microbursts may induce dangerous horizontal/vertical wind shears, which can adversely affect aircraft performance and cause property damage.

Moisture Convergence A measure of the degree to which moist air is converging into a given area, taking into account the effect of converging winds and moisture advection. Areas of persistent moisture convergence are favored regions for thunderstorm development, if other factors (e.g., instability) are favorable.

National Oceanic and Atmospheric Administration (NOAA) A branch of the U.S. Department of Commerce, it is the parent organization of the National Weather Service. It promotes global environmental stewardship, emphasizing atmospheric and marine resources.

National Weather Service (NWS) A primary branch of the National Oceanic and Atmospheric Administration, it is responsible for all aspects of observing and forecasting atmospheric conditions and their consequences, including severe weather and flood warnings.

Ozone Layer An atmospheric layer that contains a high proportion of oxygen that exists as ozone. It acts as a filtering mechanism against incoming ultraviolet radiation. It is located between the troposphere and the stratosphere, around 9.5 to 12.5 miles (15 to 20 kilometers) above the earth's surface.

Radar Acronym for RAdio Detection And Ranging. An electronic instrument used to detect distant objects and measure their range by how they scatter or reflect radio energy. Precipitation and clouds are detected by measuring the strength of the electromagnetic signal reflected back.

Relative Humidity A dimensionless ratio, expressed in percent, of the amount of atmospheric moisture present relative to the amount that would be present if the air were saturated. Since the latter amount is dependent on temperature, relative humidity is a function of both moisture content and temperature. As such, relative humidity by itself does not directly indicate the actual amount of atmospheric moisture present.

Right Mover A thunderstorm that moves appreciably to the right relative to the main steering winds and to other nearby thunderstorms. Right movers typically are associated with a high potential for severe weather.

Roll Cloud A low, horizontal tube-shaped arcus cloud associated with a thunderstorm gust front (or sometimes with a cold front). Roll clouds are relatively rare; they are completely detached from the thunderstorm base or other cloud features, thus differentiating them from the more familiar shelf clouds. Roll clouds usually appear to be "rolling" about a horizontal axis, but should not be confused with funnel clouds.

Severe Local Storm A convective storm that usually covers a relatively small geographic area, or moves in a narrow path, and is sufficiently intense to threaten life and/or property. Examples include severe thunderstorms with large hail, damaging wind, or tornadoes. Although cloud-to-ground lightning is not a criteria for severe local storms, it is acknowledged to be highly dangerous and a leading cause of deaths, injuries, and damage from thunderstorms. A thunderstorm need not be severe to generate frequent cloud-to-ground lightning.

Severe Thunderstorm A thunderstorm that produces a tornado, winds of at least 58 mph (50 knots), and/ or hail at least ¾" in diameter. Structural wind damage may imply the occurrence of a severe thunderstorm. A thunderstorm wind equal to or greater than 40 mph (35 knots) and/or hail of at least ½" is defined as approaching severe.

Shear Variation in wind speed (speed shear) and/or direction (directional shear) over a short distance. Shear usually refers to vertical wind shear, i.e., the change in wind with height, but the term also is used in Doppler radar to describe changes in radial velocity over short horizontal distances.

Shelf Cloud A low, horizontal wedge-shaped arcus cloud, associated with a thunderstorm gust front (or occasionally with a cold front, even in the absence of thunderstorms). Unlike the roll cloud, the shelf cloud is attached to the base of the parent cloud above it (usually a thunderstorm). Rising cloud motion often can be seen in the leading (outer) part of the shelf cloud, while the underside often appears turbulent, boiling, and wind-torn.

Snow Flurries Snow flurries are an intermittent light snowfall of short duration (generally light snow showers) with no measurable accumulation (trace category).

Stratiform Having extensive horizontal development, as opposed to the more vertical development characteristic of convection. Stratiform clouds cover large areas but show relatively little vertical development. Stratiform precipitation, in general, is relatively continuous and uniform in intensity (i.e., steady rain versus rain showers).

Stratocumulus Low-level clouds, existing in a relatively flat layer but having individual elements. Elements often are arranged in rows, bands, or waves. Stratocumulus often reveals the depth of the moist air at low levels, while the speed of the cloud elements can reveal the strength of the low-level jet.

Stratus A low, generally gray cloud layer with a fairly uniform base. Stratus may appear in the form of ragged patches, but otherwise does not exhibit individual cloud elements as do cumulus and stratocumulus clouds. Fog usually is a surface-based form of stratus.

Thermodynamics In general, the relationships between heat and other properties (such as temperature, pressure, density, etc.). In forecast discussions, thermodynamics usually refers to the distribution of temperature and moisture (both vertical and horizontal) as related to the diagnosis of atmospheric instability.

Tornado A violently rotating column of air, usually pendant to a cumulonimbus, with circulation reaching the ground. It nearly always starts as a funnel cloud and may be accompanied by a loud roaring noise. On a local scale, it is the most destructive of all atmospheric phenomena.

Towering Cumulus A large cumulus cloud with great vertical development, usually with a cauliflower-like appearance, but lacking the characteristic anvil of a cumulonimbus.

Troposphere The layer of the atmosphere from the earth's surface up to the tropopause, characterized by decreasing temperature with height (except, perhaps, in thin layers—*see* inversion, cap), vertical wind motion, appreciable water vapor content, and sensible weather (clouds, rain, etc.).

Tsunami An ocean wave with a long period that is formed by an underwater earthquake or landslide, or volcanic eruption. It may travel unnoticed across the ocean for thousands of miles from its point of origin and builds up to great heights over shallower water. Also known as a seismic sea wave and, incorrectly, as a tidal wave.

Updraft A small-scale current of rising air. If the air is sufficiently moist, then the moisture condenses to become a cumulus cloud or an individual tower of a towering cumulus.

Virga Streaks or wisps of precipitation falling from a cloud but evaporating before reaching the ground. In certain cases, shafts of virga may precede a microburst.

Warm Advection Transport of warm air into an area by horizontal winds. Low-level warm advection sometimes is referred to (erroneously) as overrunning. Although the two terms are not properly interchangeable, both imply the presence of lifting in low levels.

Waterspout In general, a tornado occurring over water. Specifically, it normally refers to a small, relatively weak rotating column of air over water beneath a cumulonimbus or towering cumulus cloud. Waterspouts are most common over tropical or subtropical waters.

The exact definition of waterspout is debatable. In most cases the term is reserved for small vortices over water that are not associated with storm-scale rotation (i.e., they are the water-based equivalent of landspouts). But there is sufficient justification for calling virtually any rotating column of air a waterspout if it is in contact with a water surface.

Weather Surveillance Radar (WSR-88D) The newest generation of Doppler radars, the 1988 Doppler weather radar. The radar units, with help from a set of computers, show very detailed images of precipitation and other phenomena, including air motions within a storm.

Wind Chill Increased wind speeds accelerate heat loss from exposed skin. No specific rules exist for determining when wind chill becomes dangerous. As a general rule, the threshold for potentially dangerous wind chill conditions is about –20°F.

EXPLANATION OF CLIMATIC DATA CHARTS

The following tables for each month contain comparative information for cities around the world. U.S. climatological information contained within has been furnished by the National Oceanic and Atmospheric Administration. Records of foreign data come from various sources with various lengths of record. The number of years used to determine the values for each category in the tables varies, depending in part on how long the various information has been recorded.

RECORDS *(Temperature & Precipitation)*
Records for individual cities cover extremes observed during the years observations have been taken. For cities such as New York, where several observation sites are located, the record given is the extreme highest or lowest reading obtained from all locations.

AVERAGES *(Temperature & Precipitation)*
Monthly normals are generally 30-year average values. Mathematical adjustments have been made to render the data representative of the current location. The values have been statistically determined and cannot be recreated solely from the original record.

Average Max: The average daily maximum temperature, °F.

Average Min: The average daily minimum temperature, °F.

Record Max: Highest ever recorded for month.

Record Min: Lowest ever recorded for month.

Mean Number of Days of Precipitation: Mean number of days for month with .01" or more precipitation.

Amount of Precipitation: *(Snowfall & Rainfall)* Average monthly and extreme monthly rainfall and snowfall totals.

Percentage of Sunshine: Average percentage of possible sunshine for month.

Mean Number of Clear Days: Number of days with average cloud cover of less than 3/10.

Mean Number of Cloudy Days: Number of days with 8/10 or more average cloud cover.

Relative Humidity: Average for warmest time of day.

Average Wind Speed: Average speed of the wind regardless of direction.

Degree Days: Degree day data are used to estimate amounts of energy required to maintain comfortable indoor temperature levels. Daily values are computed from each day's mean temperature ([max plus min]/2). Each degree that a day's mean temperature is below or above 65°F is counted as one heating or cooling degree day.

"T" stands for trace. "NA" stands for data not available.

Climatic data is current as of 2007.

U.S. & INTERNATIONAL CLIMATE DATA

JANUARY—U.S. CLIMATIC DATA

	TEMPERATURE (°F)				MEAN DAYS OF PRECIP	AMOUNT OF PRECIPITATION				% OF POSSIBLE SUN	MEAN		REL HUMID-ITY	AVG WIND SPEED (MPH)	DEGREE DAYS (BASE 65°F)	
	AVERAGE		RECORD			TOTAL		SNOWFALL			CLEAR DAYS	CLOUDY DAYS				
	MIN	MAX	MIN	MAX		AVG	MAX	AVG	MAX						HEATING	COOLING
Albany, NY	11.0	30.2	-28	71	12.4	2.36	7.30	16.0	47.8	45	5.5	17.4	71	9.8	1376	0
Albuquerque, NM	21.7	46.8	-17	69	3.8	0.44	2.52	2.5	9.5	72	13.0	10.2	40	8.1	955	0
Amarillo, TX	21.2	49.0	-11	83	4.0	0.50	2.67	0.0	15.9	69	12.4	11.2	50	13.0	927	0
Anchorage, AK	8.4	21.4	-35	56	7.0	0.79	2.71	10.1	36.1	40	8.3	18.2	70	6.1	1553	0
Atlanta, GA	31.5	50.4	-8	79	11.6	4.75	15.82	0.8	10.3	49	8.3	16.4	60	10.6	744	0
Atlantic City, NJ	21.4	40.4	-10	78	10.8	3.46	8.40	5.0	22.3	49	8.4	14.7	70	11.3	1057	0
Bakersfield, CA	38.6	56.9	14	82	5.9	0.86	3.90	T	3.0	NA	7.0	16.0	63	5.2	533	0
Bismarck, ND	-1.7	20.2	-45	63	7.9	0.45	1.64	7.2	25.0	54	6.8	16.5	67	10.0	1730	0
Boise, ID	21.6	36.4	-28	63	12.4	1.45	5.29	7.2	27.0	39	4.4	21.8	70	8.2	1116	0
Boston, MA	21.6	35.7	-13	72	11.7	3.59	10.55	12.6	43.3	53	9.3	15.0	57	14.0	1128	0
Buffalo, NY	17.0	30.2	-16	72	20.2	2.70	6.88	23.9	68.3	32	1.4	23.4	73	14.3	1283	0
Burlington, VT	7.5	25.1	-30	66	14.3	1.82	5.15	18.5	42.4	41	4.3	20.1	66	9.5	1510	0
Caribou, ME	-1.6	19.4	-33	53	14.4	2.42	5.68	23.8	44.5	NA	6.8	17.3	71	12.4	1739	0
Casper, WY	12.0	32.8	-40	60	7.4	0.55	1.42	10.1	39.3	NA	6.5	16.8	60	16.5	1321	0
Charleston, SC	37.7	57.8	6	83	9.8	3.45	8.92	0.1	1.9	58	8.9	15.6	55	9.2	548	15
Charleston, WV	23.0	41.2	-16	81	15.6	2.91	9.11	10.4	39.5	NA	3.5	20.7	65	7.6	1020	0
Charlotte, NC	29.6	49.0	-5	79	10.2	3.71	10.39	2.0	13.5	55	9.1	15.5	56	7.9	797	0
Chicago, IL	12.9	29.0	-27	67	11.3	1.53	4.84	11.1	42.5	42	6.9	18.2	67	11.6	1364	0
Cincinnati, OH	19.5	36.6	-25	77	12.1	2.59	13.68	7.5	31.5	41	5.1	19.7	68	10.7	1144	0
Cleveland, OH	17.6	31.9	-20	73	16.5	2.04	7.01	16.6	42.8	31	27.0	23.5	70	12.4	1246	0
Dallas, TX	32.7	54.1	-3	93	7.0	1.83	9.07	1.4	12.1	53	9.8	15.5	59	11.1	670	0
Denver, CO	16.1	43.2	-29	76	5.8	0.50	2.35	7.7	23.7	71	10.0	11.8	46	8.8	1094	0
Des Moines, IA	10.7	28.1	-30	67	7.6	0.96	4.38	8.6	37.0	51	7.8	16.2	68	11.7	1414	0
Detroit, MI	15.6	30.3	-21	67	13.0	1.76	5.02	9.6	29.6	40	4.3	20.0	70	11.7	1305	0
El Paso, TX	29.4	56.1	-8	80	4.1	0.40	1.84	1.3	8.3	77	13.9	9.8	36	8.6	688	0
Ely, NV	9.4	39.7	-27	68	6.8	0.70	2.08	24.8	—	67	8.6	14.9	55	10.2	1252	0
Grand Rapids, MI	14.7	29.0	-22	66	16.3	1.83	6.00	24.1	46.8	30	2.5	23.6	72	11.4	1339	0
Hartford, CT	15.8	33.2	-26	70	10.7	3.41	9.61	12.1	43.1	57	7.7	15.0	61	9.0	1252	0
Helena, MT	9.6	29.6	-42	63	8.2	0.63	3.75	9.1	35.6	46	4.6	20.5	61	6.9	1407	0
Honolulu, HI	65.6	80.1	53	88	10.1	3.55	18.36	0.0	—	62	9.1	8.9	63	9.8	0	245
Houston, TX	39.7	61.0	5	84	10.3	3.29	13.11	0.2	3.0	43	7.3	18.3	65	8.2	468	16
Indianapolis, IN	17.2	33.7	-27	71	11.9	2.32	12.69	6.2	30.6	41	5.9	19.1	72	11.0	1225	0
Jackson, MS	32.7	55.6	-5	85	11.0	5.24	14.10	.07	11.7	47	7.8	17.2	71	8.7	656	8
Jacksonville, FL	40.5	64.2	7	85	7.8	3.31	10.21	T	T	58	9.2	13.5	74	8.3	421	31
Kansas City, MO	16.7	34.7	-20	75	8.2	1.09	5.52	5.8	30.5	59	9.6	15.4	64	11.0	1218	0
Las Vegas, NV	33.0	57.3	8	77	3.0	0.48	3.00	1.2	10.7	77	13.9	10.9	30	7.4	605	0
Lexington, KY	22.4	39.1	-21	80	12.6	2.86	16.65	6.2	21.9	NA	5.8	19.3	69	11.2	1060	0
Lincoln, NE	10.1	32.4	-33	73	6.5	0.54	3.70	6.5	23.0	57	9.2	15.6	70	10.1	1355	0
Little Rock, AR	29.4	47.6	-8	83	9.7	3.21	18.04	2.3	19.4	46	8.6	16.3	64	8.7	822	0
Los Angeles, CA	48.9	67.7	23	95	6.1	2.92	14.94	T	2.0	69	12.0	10.8	56	6.7	222	14
Lubbock, TX	24.6	52.9	-16	87	3.7	0.39	4.05	2.5	25.3	66	12.6	11.9	47	12.1	812	0
Marquette, MI	3.3	20.5	-33	57	17.5	2.17	6.61	26.7	91.7	32	NA	NA	NA	NA	1646	0
Medford, OR	30.4	45.7	-3	71	13.5	2.69	6.67	3.6	22.6	NA	2.6	23.5	72	4.1	834	0
Memphis, TN	30.9	48.5	-8	79	10.1	3.73	17.56	2.3	15.1	50	7.9	17.2	63	10.3	784	0
Miami, FL	59.2	75.2	30	88	6.5	2.01	7.93	0.0	—	67	9.6	8.5	60	9.4	88	156

	TEMPERATURE (°F)				MEAN DAYS OF PRECIP	AMOUNT OF PRECIPITATION				% OF POSSIBLE SUN	MEAN		REL HUMID-ITY	AVG WIND SPEED (MPH)	DEGREE DAYS (BASE 65°F)	
	AVERAGE		RECORD			TOTAL		SNOWFALL			CLEAR DAYS	CLOUDY DAYS				
	MIN	MAX	MIN	MAX		AVG	MAX	AVG	MAX						HEATING	COOLING
Milwaukee, WI	11.6	26.1	-26	62	11.1	1.60	5.38	13.0	52.6	44	7.2	17.7	68	12.8	1429	0
Minneapolis, MN	2.8	20.7	-34	58	8.8	0.95	3.63	9.9	46.4	52	8.4	15.3	66	10.4	1649	0
Montgomery, AL	35.8	56.3	0	83	10.7	4.68	17.78	0.2	6.0	48	7.4	17.1	64	7.8	594	8
Nashville, TN	26.5	45.9	-17	78	11.1	3.58	14.75	4.2	18.8	41	6.3	18.4	63	9.2	893	0
New Orleans, LA	41.8	60.8	14	83	10.1	5.05	19.28	0.0	5.0	48	6.7	16.9	66	9.4	450	25
New York, NY	25.3	37.6	-6	72	11.2	3.42	10.52	7.6	27.4	50	8.1	13.7	60	10.7	1039	0
Norfolk, VA	30.9	47.3	-7	80	10.4	3.78	9.93	2.9	22.7	56	9.2	15.4	67	11.5	803	0
Oklahoma City, OK	25.2	46.7	-11	83	5.5	1.13	5.68	2.9	17.3	59	10.3	14.6	60	12.9	902	0
Orlando, FL	48.6	70.8	19	87	6.3	2.30	7.23	T	T	NA	9.4	11.1	56	9.0	234	70
Philadelphia, PA	22.8	37.9	-7	74	11.0	3.21	8.86	6.4	33.7	50	7.4	16.1	59	10.3	1073	0
Phoenix, AZ	39.4	65.2	16	88	3.8	.73	5.25	T	1.0	78	13.8	10.3	32	5.3	394	0
Pittsburgh, PA	18.5	33.7	-22	75	16.4	2.54	7.15	12.1	40.2	33	3.0	21.9	65	10.7	1206	0
Portland, OR	33.7	45.4	-2	66	18.6	5.35	13.71	3.9	41.4	27	2.8	25.0	76	10.0	787	0
Providence, RI	19.1	36.6	-13	69	11.1	3.88	11.66	9.9	37.4	57	9.9	14.4	63	11.3	1150	0
Raleigh, NC	28.8	48.9	-9	80	9.9	3.48	7.52	0.0	25.8	54	9.3	14.7	55	8.6	809	0
Reno, NV	20.7	45.1	-19	71	6.1	1.07	6.76	5.9	65.7	65	8.5	15.4	51	5.6	995	0
Sacramento, CA	37.7	52.7	19	72	10.2	3.73	15.04	T	4.0	45	6.3	18.7	71	7.6	614	0
Salt Lake City, UT	19.3	36.4	-22	63	9.9	1.11	3.90	13.2	33.6	46	5.5	18.9	68	7.7	1150	0
San Antonio, TX	37.9	60.8	0	89	8.1	1.71	8.52	0.2	15.9	48	8.9	15.9	57	9.2	494	8
San Diego, CA	48.9	65.9	25	88	6.9	1.80	9.09	T	T	72	12.4	11.2	56	5.8	245	9
San Francisco, CA	45.8	56.3	24	79	10.8	4.06	24.36	0.0	1.5	56	8.6	14.7	66	7.1	431	0
Seattle, WA	35.2	45.0	0	67	19.0	5.38	12.92	6.0	57.2	24	2.6	24.5	74	9.9	772	0
Sioux Falls, SD	3.3	24.3	-38	66	6.2	0.51	2.23	6.5	22.2	NA	8.1	15.2	71	11.0	1587	0
Spokane, WA	20.8	33.2	-30	62	14.2	1.98	4.96	17.3	56.9	26	3.2	23.5	78	8.6	1175	0
St. Louis, MO	20.8	37.7	-22	77	8.6	1.81	9.00	5.4	23.9	52	7.5	17.1	71	10.6	1107	0
Tampa, FL	50.0	69.8	21	86	6.3	1.99	8.02	0.0	0.2	64	9.5	11.6	59	8.6	234	76
Washington, DC	26.8	42.3	-18	79	10.3	2.72	7.83	5.1	31.5	48	7.6	16.2	54	10.0	942	0
Wichita, KS	19.2	39.8	-15	75	5.6	0.79	6.29	4.5	19.7	59	10.1	14.8	65	12.2	1101	0

INTERNATIONAL DATA

	AVG HIGH TEMP	AVG LOW TEMP	AVG PRECIP	DAYS WITH MEASURABLE PRECIP		AVG HIGH TEMP	AVG LOW TEMP	AVG PRECIP	DAYS WITH MEASURABLE PRECIP
Cape Town, South Africa	78	60	0.7	NA	Nairobi, Kenya	80	55	1.9	5
Delhi, India	70	44	0.9	NA	Paris, France	43	34	2.2	17
Hong Kong, China	64	56	1.3	NA	Rio de Janeiro, Brazil	84	73	4.9	13
Jerusalem, Israel	55	41	5.2	NA	Rome, Italy	52	40	2.8	8
London, United Kingdom	43	36	2.1	15	Sydney, Australia	78	65	3.9	13
Manila, Philippines	87	68	0.6	4	Tahiti, Society Islands	89	72	9.9	NA
Melbourne, Australia	78	57	1.9	8	Tokyo, Japan	47	29	1.9	6
Montreal, Canada	22	6	2.8	17	Toronto, Canada	28	12	2.0	14
Moscow, Russia	21	12	1.2	16					

FEBRUARY—U.S. CLIMATIC DATA

	TEMPERATURE (°F) AVERAGE		RECORD		MEAN DAYS OF PRECIP	AMOUNT OF PRECIPITATION TOTAL		SNOWFALL		% OF POSSIBLE SUN	MEAN CLEAR DAYS	CLOUDY DAYS	REL HUMID-ITY	AVG WIND SPEED (MPH)	DEGREE DAYS (BASE 65°F) HEATING	COOLING
	MIN	MAX	MIN	MAX		AVG	MAX	AVG	MAX							
Albany, NY	13.8	33.2	-22	68	10.6	2.27	5.19	14.3	40.7	51	5.4	15.4	66	10.3	1162	0
Albuquerque, NM	26.4	53.5	-6	75	4.0	0.46	2.60	2.0	10.3	73	11.3	9.2	32	8.9	700	0
Amarillo, TX	25.5	52.8	-16	88	4.4	0.61	2.93	0.0	28.7	69	10.4	10.0	49	14.1	722	0
Anchorage, AK	11.5	25.8	-38	57	8.3	0.78	3.07	11.7	52.1	44	6.6	18.0	66	6.7	1296	0
Atlanta, GA	34.5	55.0	-9	80	10.1	4.81	12.77	0.5	11.6	54	8.0	13.8	54	10.9	566	0
Atlantic City, NJ	23.5	42.5	-11	77	9.7	3.06	7.44	5.5	35.2	52	7.7	13.6	68	11.6	896	0
Bakersfield, CA	42.6	63.9	20	85	6.2	1.06	5.36	T	T	NA	7.6	12.1	51	5.8	331	0
Bismarck, ND	5.1	26.4	-45	69	6.8	0.43	1.74	6.4	25.6	54	5.2	15.3	67	9.9	1380	0
Boise, ID	27.5	44.2	-15	71	10.5	1.07	6.49	3.7	25.2	50	4.3	17.6	60	9.2	815	0
Boston, MA	23.0	37.5	-18	70	10.6	3.62	7.81	11.6	41.6	56	8.4	13.2	56	13.9	972	0
Buffalo, NY	17.4	31.6	-20	71	16.9	2.31	5.90	17.9	54.2	38	2.0	20.7	70	13.7	1134	0
Burlington, VT	8.9	27.5	-30	62	11.6	1.63	5.38	16.7	34.3	47	4.4	17.5	65	9.2	1310	0
Caribou, ME	0.7	23.0	-41	59	12.5	1.92	4.13	21.9	41.0	NA	5.9	16.1	69	12.0	1487	0
Casper, WY	16.0	37.0	-32	68	7.9	0.60	1.42	9.7	23.8	NA	6.1	13.9	56	15.2	1078	0
Charleston, SC	40.0	61.0	7	87	8.9	3.30	10.45	0.0	7.1	62	9.1	12.6	51	10.0	414	8
Charleston, WV	25.7	45.3	-12	80	13.6	3.04	8.10	8.5	21.8	NA	4.3	17.8	61	7.6	826	0
Charlotte, NC	31.9	53.0	-5	82	9.6	3.84	8.58	1.9	17.4	60	8.9	13.0	52	8.4	630	0
Chicago, IL	17.2	33.5	-21	71	9.6	1.36	5.98	7.8	27.8	44	6.1	15.9	65	11.4	1109	0
Cincinnati, OH	22.7	40.8	-17	76	11.1	2.68	8.87	5.3	21.4	51	5.2	17.4	64	10.4	930	0
Cleveland, OH	19.3	35.0	-16	74	14.4	2.19	7.73	13.8	30.5	37	3.0	19.8	68	12.1	1058	0
Dallas, TX	36.9	58.9	2	95	6.4	2.18	7.68	1.1	13.5	58	9.9	12.5	53	11.9	484	5
Denver, CO	20.2	46.6	-30	77	5.7	0.57	2.01	7.4	22.1	71	8.2	11.4	42	9.1	885	0
Des Moines, IA	15.6	33.7	-26	78	7.2	1.11	3.20	7.2	21.3	54	7.5	14.9	66	11.6	1128	0
Detroit, MI	17.6	33.3	-20	70	10.9	1.74	6.41	8.1	38.4	47	4.9	16.5	65	11.4	1109	0
El Paso, TX	33.9	62.2	5	86	2.8	0.41	1.92	0.7	8.9	82	14.0	6.8	26	9.4	473	0
Ely, NV	16.4	43.6	-30	67	7.1	0.65	2.19	0.0	20.0	67	6.9	14.4	50	10.4	994	0
Grand Rapids, MI	15.8	31.6	-24	69	11.9	1.42	7.87	11.2	35.5	39	3.5	18.9	68	10.5	1156	0
Hartford, CT	18.6	36.4	-24	73	10.4	3.23	7.27	12.1	32.7	58	6.5	13.8	60	9.4	1050	0
Helena, MT	15.9	36.9	-42	69	6.4	0.41	1.69	6.0	31.1	54	4.0	17.7	54	7.5	1081	0
Honolulu, HI	65.4	80.5	53	88	9.4	2.21	13.68	0.0	—	64	7.5	8.1	59	10.5	0	224
Houston, TX	42.6	65.3	6	91	7.3	2.96	9.01	0.2	20.0	51	7.7	14.3	59	8.8	322	11
Indianapolis, IN	20.9	38.3	-21	76	10.1	2.46	7.28	5.8	21.7	50	5.7	16.1	70	10.8	991	0
Jackson, MS	35.7	60.1	10	89	8.9	4.70	12.94	0.2	9.1	55	8.5	13.5	63	8.7	485	6
Jacksonville, FL	43.3	67.0	10	88	7.8	3.93	11.12	T	1.9	62	8.9	11.9	68	9.2	296	22
Kansas City, MO	21.8	40.6	-22	81	6.6	1.10	6.76	4.3	20.7	56	7.8	14.1	62	11.6	946	0
Las Vegas, NV	38.8	63.3	-17	87	2.6	0.48	2.89	0.0	4.1	80	12.5	8.7	26	8.5	389	0
Lexington, KY	25.3	43.6	-20	80	11.2	3.21	11.06	4.8	17.4	NA	6.1	16.5	64	11.1	854	0
Lincoln, NE	15.1	37.9	-26	84	5.2	0.72	3.06	6.2	26.1	57	8.0	13.9	67	10.5	1075	0
Little Rock, AR	33.6	52.7	-12	87	8.9	3.53	12.74	1.5	15.6	54	9.1	13.5	59	9.1	610	0
Los Angeles, CA	50.6	69.4	28	95	6.1	3.07	13.68	T	T	72	11.3	10.7	59	7.4	170	32
Lubbock, TX	28.6	57.6	-17	89	4.0	0.68	5.83	3.2	16.8	67	11.0	9.9	41	13.4	613	0
Marquette, MI	4.0	23.9	-34	69	13.2	1.73	5.35	22.3	54.3	37	NA	NA	NA	NA	1428	0
Medford, OR	32.2	53.3	6	79	11.4	1.93	5.67	1.3	17.5	NA	3.4	19.1	59	4.6	622	0
Memphis, TN	34.8	53.5	-11	81	9.5	4.35	10.50	1.3	10.3	54	7.9	14.7	59	10.3	582	0
Miami, FL	60.4	76.5	27	89	6.1	2.08	8.07	0.0	—	65	8.5	7.9	57	10.1	51	149

	TEMPERATURE (°F) AVERAGE		RECORD		MEAN DAYS OF PRECIP	AMOUNT OF PRECIPITATION TOTAL		SNOWFALL		% OF POSSIBLE SUN	MEAN CLEAR DAYS	CLOUDY DAYS	REL HUMID-ITY	AVG WIND SPEED (MPH)	DEGREE DAYS (BASE 65°F) HEATING	COOLING
	MIN	MAX	MIN	MAX		AVG	MAX	AVG	MAX							
Milwaukee, WI	15.9	30.1	-26	68	9.5	1.45	5.39	9.3	42.0	47	6.6	15.7	67	12.6	1176	0
Minneapolis, MN	9.2	26.6	-33	64	7.5	0.88	3.25	8.4	26.5	58	7.8	13.6	65	10.5	1319	0
Montgomery, AL	38.8	60.8	-5	85	9.3	5.48	13.38	0.1	4.1	54	8.0	13.8	57	8.3	426	0
Nashville, TN	29.9	50.8	-13	84	10.7	3.81	12.37	3.2	18.9	47	6.9	15.4	59	9.4	689	0
New Orleans, LA	44.4	64.1	7	85	9.1	6.01	13.85	0.1	8.2	53	7.9	13.7	63	9.8	316	17
New York, NY	26.9	40.3	-15	75	9.8	3.27	6.87	8.6	27.9	55	8.3	11.2	58	10.8	879	0
Norfolk, VA	32.3	49.7	-5	82	10.0	3.47	8.21	2.8	18.9	59	8.6	13.7	65	11.9	672	0
Oklahoma City, OK	29.6	52.1	-17	92	6.3	1.56	4.63	2.5	12.9	60	9.1	12.2	54	13.3	675	0
Orlando, FL	49.7	72.7	28	90	7.0	3.02	8.32	0.0	—	NA	8.8	10.7	53	9.6	164	58
Philadelphia, PA	24.8	41.0	-11	79	9.3	2.79	6.87	6.7	31.5	53	7.2	13.7	56	11.0	896	0
Phoenix, AZ	42.5	69.7	22	92	3.9	0.59	4.64	0.0	0.6	80	12.6	8.9	27	5.9	269	20
Pittsburgh, PA	20.3	36.9	-20	77	14.1	2.39	6.52	10.0	25.3	38	3.3	19.0	62	10.6	1016	0
Portland, OR	36.1	51.0	-3	71	16.5	3.85	13.36	0.6	20.0	37	2.6	22.2	68	9.2	599	0
Providence, RI	20.9	38.3	-17	72	10.1	3.61	7.20	10.0	30.9	57	7.9	12.8	61	11.6	988	0
Raleigh, NC	31.3	52.6	-2	84	9.7	3.69	9.73	0.0	17.9	58	8.8	13.2	51	8.9	644	0
Reno, NV	24.2	51.7	-12	76	5.9	0.99	4.99	4.7	32.5	68	6.8	14.0	40	6.2	756	0
Sacramento, CA	41.4	60.0	21	80	8.8	2.87	9.25	0.1	2.0	61	7.5	13.8	61	7.7	400	0
Salt Lake City, UT	24.6	43.6	-30	69	8.8	1.23	4.89	9.5	30.0	55	5.2	16.0	59	8.2	865	0
San Antonio, TX	41.3	65.7	4	100	7.7	1.81	7.88	0.2	4.2	53	8.4	13.8	52	9.8	332	10
San Diego, CA	50.7	66.5	34	90	6.0	1.53	9.05	0.0	—	72	10.6	10.2	58	6.4	189	10
San Francisco, CA	48.7	60.0	25	81	9.8	2.95	14.89	T	3.7	62	7.8	13.1	65	8.5	297	0
Seattle, WA	37.4	49.5	1	74	16.2	3.99	9.11	1.4	35.4	37	2.5	21.7	67	9.7	602	0
Sioux Falls, SD	9.7	29.6	-42	70	6.5	0.64	4.05	8.5	48.4	NA	6.9	14.6	70	11.1	1268	0
Spokane, WA	25.9	40.6	-24	63	11.7	1.49	5.62	7.3	37.8	38	3.2	20.1	69	9.1	888	0
St. Louis, MO	25.1	42.6	-18	85	8.2	2.12	8.94	4.5	23.5	53	7.0	14.8	66	10.9	871	0
Tampa, FL	51.6	71.4	22	88	6.9	3.08	10.85	T	0.1	66	9.1	10.2	56	9.4	160	62
Washington, DC	29.1	45.9	-15	84	8.7	2.71	6.84	5.6	35.2	52	7.6	14.1	52	10.3	770	0
Wichita, KS	23.7	45.9	-22	87	5.2	0.96	4.61	4.4	20.5	60	8.3	12.8	60	12.8	846	0

INTERNATIONAL DATA

	AVG HIGH TEMP	AVG LOW TEMP	AVG PRECIP	DAYS WITH MEASURABLE PRECIP		AVG HIGH TEMP	AVG LOW TEMP	AVG PRECIP	DAYS WITH MEASURABLE PRECIP
Cape Town, South Africa	79	60	0.6	NA	Nairobi, Kenya	82	56	1.4	4
Delhi, India	75	49	0.7	NA	Paris, France	45	34	1.8	14
Hong Kong, China	63	55	1.8	NA	Rio de Janeiro, Brazil	85	73	4.8	11
Jerusalem, Israel	56	42	5.2	NA	Rome, Italy	55	42	2.4	9
London, United Kingdom	44	36	1.6	13	Sydney, Australia	78	65	4.5	13
Manila, Philippines	89	69	0.3	3	Tahiti, Society Islands	89	72	9.6	NA
Melbourne, Australia	78	58	2.0	7	Tokyo, Japan	48	31	2.9	7
Montreal, Canada	24	8	2.6	14	Toronto, Canada	29	13	1.8	12
Moscow, Russia	22	12	1.1	12					

242

MARCH—U.S. CLIMATIC DATA

	TEMPERATURE (°F) AVERAGE MIN	MAX	RECORD MIN	MAX	MEAN DAYS OF PRECIP	AMOUNT OF PRECIPITATION TOTAL AVG	MAX	SNOWFALL AVG	MAX	% OF POSSIBLE SUN	MEAN CLEAR DAYS	CLOUDY DAYS	REL HUMID-ITY	AVG WIND SPEED (MPH)	DEGREE DAYS (BASE 65°F) HEATING	COOLING
Albany, NY	24.5	44.0	-21	89	12.1	2.93	7.37	11.9	50.9	53	6.0	17.1	61	10.7	952	0
Albuquerque, NM	32.2	61.4	8	85	4.5	0.54	2.18	1.9	13.9	73	11.3	9.6	24	10.2	561	0
Amarillo, TX	32.7	61.6	-3	96	4.6	0.96	4.14	2.4	21.5	71	11.4	11.0	42	15.5	555	0
Anchorage, AK	18.1	33.1	-24	56	7.7	0.69	2.76	9.1	31.0	53	7.4	17.9	56	6.7	1218	0
Atlanta, GA	42.5	64.3	8	89	11.7	5.77	13.28	0.4	7.9	58	8.9	14.9	51	10.9	365	8
Atlantic City, NJ	31.3	51.6	5	87	10.8	3.62	8.82	2.9	23.6	53	7.7	15.2	65	12.1	729	0
Bakersfield, CA	45.8	68.9	21	94	6.6	1.04	4.61	0.0	1.5	NA	10.1	11.4	43	6.5	246	11
Bismarck, ND	17.8	38.5	-36	81	8.2	0.77	3.27	8.4	31.1	59	5.4	17.2	63	11.0	1141	0
Boise, ID	31.9	52.9	5	81	9.7	1.29	7.66	1.9	18.9	62	6.0	17.8	45	10.1	701	0
Boston, MA	31.3	45.8	-8	89	11.9	3.69	11.00	7.8	38.9	57	7.8	15.3	57	13.8	818	0
Buffalo, NY	25.9	41.7	-7	81	16.2	2.68	7.03	11.8	38.5	45	3.6	19.9	67	13.4	967	0
Burlington, VT	22.0	39.3	-24	84	13.1	2.23	4.53	12.4	47.6	50	5.6	18.6	63	9.4	1063	0
Caribou, ME	14.9	34.3	-28	73	12.9	2.43	5.13	20.4	47.1	NA	6.5	17.0	68	12.9	1252	0
Casper, WY	21.8	45.2	-21	74	9.6	0.95	2.43	15.2	36.2	NA	5.8	16.5	48	14.0	977	0
Charleston, SC	47.5	68.6	15	94	10.4	4.34	11.11	0.1	2.0	67	9.1	13.7	51	10.1	239	25
Charleston, WV	35.0	56.7	0	92	15.2	3.63	8.94	4.9	21.4	NA	4.4	18.8	54	8.4	592	0
Charlotte, NC	39.4	62.3	4	91	11.4	4.43	11.13	1.5	19.3	63	9.1	13.8	51	8.9	437	0
Chicago, IL	28.5	45.8	-12	88	12.7	2.69	5.91	7.6	24.7	50	4.7	17.6	61	11.8	862	0
Cincinnati, OH	33.1	53.0	-11	88	13.2	4.24	12.8	4.5	13.9	28	5.0	19.3	61	11.1	682	0
Cleveland, OH	28.2	46.3	-5	83	15.6	2.91	8.31	9.9	26.3	44	4.4	20.2	63	12.4	859	0
Dallas, TX	45.6	67.8	11	96	7.3	2.77	9.53	0.2	4.3	59	9.6	13.7	51	13.0	286	29
Denver, CO	25.8	52.2	-11	84	8.7	1.28	4.56	13.1	35.2	70	7.8	12.9	41	9.8	806	0
Des Moines, IA	27.6	46.9	-22	91	10.2	2.33	5.82	7.0	28.0	54	6.6	17.1	60	12.9	859	0
Detroit, MI	27.0	44.4	-4	82	13.2	2.55	5.63	6.8	30.2	51	5.3	18.3	62	11.7	908	0
El Paso, TX	40.2	69.9	14	93	2.4	0.29	2.26	0.5	7.3	85	14.8	8.1	21	11.4	316	10
Ely, NV	20.7	48.4	-13	76	8.5	0.96	2.40	9.9	24.8	70	7.6	15.2	43	10.7	942	0
Grand Rapids, MI	25.4	42.8	-13	82	12.8	2.63	6.88	11.0	36.0	44	4.5	19.6	64	11.1	958	0
Hartford, CT	28.1	46.8	-6	89	11.5	3.63	9.21	10.9	43.3	56	6.4	16.2	57	10.0	853	0
Helena, MT	22.3	44.8	-30	77	8.6	0.73	2.39	7.4	26.6	50	3.6	19.1	46	8.5	973	0
Honolulu, HI	67.2	81.6	55	88	9.0	2.20	20.79	0.0	—	68	7.3	9.6	58	11.5	0	291
Houston, TX	50.0	71.1	21	96	9.8	2.92	10.66	0.0	0.8	46	6.5	17.9	50	9.5	187	50
Indianapolis, IN	31.9	50.9	-7	85	13.1	3.79	10.95	3.7	30.4	50	5.6	16.3	61	11.7	732	0
Jackson, MS	44.1	69.3	15	95	10.5	5.82	15.13	0.3	5.3	59	8.5	15.1	59	9.3	285	28
Jacksonville, FL	49.2	73.0	23	91	8.0	3.68	12.52	T	T	67	9.2	12.5	65	9.2	169	48
Kansas City, MO	32.6	52.8	-10	91	10.7	2.51	9.08	3.9	40.2	58	6.3	16.9	59	12.5	691	0
Las Vegas, NV	43.8	68.8	19	92	2.9	0.42	4.80	0.0	0.1	83	13.8	8.2	22	10.1	292	22
Lexington, KY	35.3	55.3	-2	86	13.1	4.40	13.82	2.8	17.7	NA	5.5	18.0	58	11.5	611	0
Lincoln, NE	26.8	50.3	-19	91	8.8	2.09	6.65	6.5	21.3	56	7.8	15.7	59	11.9	818	0
Little Rock, AR	42.6	62.7	11	91	10.4	4.97	10.43	0.6	8.0	57	8.6	15.4	55	9.8	395	13
Los Angeles, CA	51.8	69.5	31	99	5.8	2.61	12.36	0.0	—	73	11.6	10.7	61	8.1	169	36
Lubbock, TX	34.6	66.0	-2	95	3.7	0.89	5.94	1.6	16.5	72	11.6	0.6	33	13.4	437	10
Marquette, MI	13.6	33.5	-30	71	14.8	2.77	6.08	21.2	60.6	44	NA	NA	NA	NA	1283	0
Medford, OR	35.4	58.5	14	86	11.7	1.82	5.54	0.8	8.1	NA	5.2	19.3	50	5.3	558	0
Memphis, TN	43.0	63.2	12	87	11.0	5.41	13.04	1.0	18.5	56	8.1	16.3	56	11.1	383	14
Miami, FL	64.2	79.1	32	93	5.7	2.39	10.57	0.0	—	77	8.7	8.1	56	10.4	14	221
Milwaukee, WI	26.2	40.4	-10	81	11.9	2.67	6.93	9.2	36.3	50	6.0	17.2	65	13.0	983	0
Minneapolis, MN	22.7	39.2	-32	83	10.3	1.94	4.75	10.6	40.0	55	6.9	16.4	62	11.3	1054	0
Montgomery, AL	45.7	68.6	17	90	10.3	6.26	16.51	T	1.4	59	8.0	15.1	55	8.4	263	21
Nashville, TN	39.1	61.2	2	89	12.1	4.85	12.35	1.5	21.5	52	7.6	16.6	53	10.0	469	10
New Orleans, LA	51.6	71.6	25	90	9.0	4.90	21.09	T	T	57	7.7	15.1	60	9.9	162	56
New York, NY	34.8	50.0	3	86	11.5	4.08	10.41	5.1	30.5	56	8.8	12.1	55	11.0	701	0
Norfolk, VA	39.3	57.9	8	92	11.0	3.70	9.01	1.2	19.1	63	9.0	14.6	62	12.4	508	0
Oklahoma City, OK	38.5	62.0	1	97	7.2	2.71	8.02	1.5	20.7	63	9.6	13.4	49	14.6	464	9
Orlando, FL	55.2	78.0	25	92	7.5	3.21	11.38	0.0	—	NA	9.3	11.2	50	9.9	65	117
Philadelphia, PA	33.2	51.6	5	87	11.1	3.46	9.10	4.0	15.2	55	7.5	15.3	53	11.4	701	0
Phoenix, AZ	46.7	74.5	25	100	3.5	0.81	4.82	T	0.2	83	14.6	8.5	24	6.7	187	51
Pittsburgh, PA	29.8	49.0	-1	84	16.1	3.41	6.10	8.7	34.1	44	4.0	20.1	58	10.9	794	0
Portland, OR	38.6	56.0	19	83	17.2	3.56	12.76	0.5	15.2	46	3.1	23.6	60	8.3	549	0
Providence, RI	28.8	46.1	1	90	11.8	4.05	8.84	8.3	31.6	57	8.6	14.9	60	12.2	856	0
Raleigh, NC	38.7	62.1	11	94	10.2	3.77	7.78	1.5	17.8	62	9.6	13.8	49	9.4	458	0
Reno, NV	29.2	56.3	-3	83	6.4	0.71	4.15	4.9	29.0	75	8.2	13.6	34	7.7	688	0
Sacramento, CA	43.2	64.0	26	88	8.4	2.57	10.00	T	2.0	72	10.4	12.5	53	8.8	357	0
Salt Lake City, UT	31.4	52.2	0	78	9.9	1.91	4.66	10.4	41.9	63	7.0	15.7	47	9.3	719	0
San Antonio, TX	49.7	73.5	19	100	7.0	1.52	7.24	T	1.5	57	8.5	15.2	47	10.6	167	64
San Diego, CA	52.8	66.3	36	99	7.2	1.77	7.20	0.0	—	71	11.2	10.5	59	7.3	177	9
San Francisco, CA	49.0	60.8	30	87	9.7	3.07	9.04	T	1.0	69	9.7	12.6	63	10.4	313	0
Seattle, WA	38.5	52.7	11	81	17.1	3.54	8.40	1.4	18.2	49	3.1	22.1	62	9.9	601	0
Sioux Falls, SD	22.6	42.3	-23	88	8.7	1.64	4.98	10.0	31.5	NA	6.1	17.3	64	12.5	1008	0
Spokane, WA	29.6	47.7	-10	74	11.3	1.49	3.79	4.1	16.4	53	4.3	18.9	55	9.5	815	0
St. Louis, MO	35.5	54.6	-5	92	11.6	3.58	9.52	4.4	28.8	53	6.5	16.5	61	11.9	617	0
Tampa, FL	56.5	76.6	29	91	6.8	3.01	12.64	T	T	71	10.2	10.8	55	9.6	84	128
Washington, DC	37.7	56.5	4	93	11.0	3.17	8.84	2.3	19.3	55	7.3	15.1	50	10.9	552	0
Wichita, KS	33.6	57.2	-3	92	7.8	2.43	9.17	2.7	16.8	61	8.8	15.1	52	14.2	608	0

INTERNATIONAL DATA

	AVG HIGH TEMP	AVG LOW TEMP	AVG PRECIP	DAYS WITH MEASURABLE PRECIP
Cape Town, South Africa	77	58	0.9	NA
Delhi, India	87	58	0.5	NA
Hong Kong, China	67	60	2.9	NA
Jerusalem, Israel	65	46	2.5	NA
London, United Kingdom	50	38	1.5	11
Manila, Philippines	92	71	0.3	3
Melbourne, Australia	75	55	2.1	9
Montreal, Canada	35	20	2.9	13
Moscow, Russia	34	24	1.3	9
Nairobi, Kenya	82	57	3.4	8
Paris, France	54	38	1.4	12
Rio de Janeiro, Brazil	83	72	5.1	12
Rome, Italy	59	45	2.2	8
Sydney, Australia	76	63	5.2	14
Tahiti, Society Islands	89	72	16.9	NA
Tokyo, Japan	54	36	4.2	10
Toronto, Canada	38	23	2.4	13

APRIL—U.S. CLIMATIC DATA

	TEMPERATURE (°F) AVERAGE MIN	MAX	RECORD MIN	MAX	MEAN DAYS OF PRECIP	AMOUNT OF PRECIPITATION TOTAL AVG	MAX	SNOWFALL AVG	MAX	% OF POSSIBLE SUN	MEAN CLEAR DAYS	CLOUDY DAYS	REL HUMIDITY	AVG WIND SPEED (MPH)	DEGREE DAYS (BASE 65°F) HEATING	COOLING
Albany, NY	35.1	57.5	9	93	12.2	2.99	7.95	3.1	17.7	53	5.8	16.1	55	10.6	558	0
Albuquerque, NM	39.6	70.8	18	89	3.3	0.52	4.20	0.5	8.1	77	12.8	7.8	18	11.1	301	7
Amarillo, TX	42.1	71.5	13	98	5.0	0.99	6.45	.05	8.3	73	11.6	9.6	38	15.5	266	20
Anchorage, AK	28.6	42.8	−21	72	7.1	0.67	1.91	5.5	27.6	52	5.3	18.3	54	7.2	876	0
Atlanta, GA	50.2	72.7	25	93	9.1	4.26	11.86	T	1.5	65	9.8	12.0	51	10.1	138	33
Atlantic City, NJ	39.3	60.7	12	94	10.7	3.56	7.95	0.3	6.0	55	7.4	13.2	64	11.9	450	0
Bakersfield, CA	50.1	75.9	30	101	4.2	0.57	2.39	0.0	—	NA	13.0	4.2	33	7.1	144	84
Bismarck, ND	31.0	54.9	−12	93	8.1	1.67	5.71	3.9	18.7	59	5.9	15.5	48	12.1	660	0
Boise, ID	36.7	61.4	11	92	8.2	1.24	4.73	0.7	8.0	66	6.7	14.7	36	10.2	477	0
Boston, MA	40.2	55.9	11	94	11.3	3.60	9.57	0.9	28.3	57	7.3	14.5	53	13.3	507	0
Buffalo, NY	36.2	54.2	5	94	14.3	2.87	5.90	3.3	15.7	52	4.9	16.9	58	12.8	594	0
Burlington, VT	34.2	53.6	2	91	12.4	2.76	6.55	3.9	21.3	49	5.1	17.3	58	9.3	633	0
Caribou, ME	29.0	46.7	−2	86	13.0	2.45	5.26	8.6	36.4	NA	5.0	18.0	65	11.7	813	0
Casper, WY	29.5	56.1	−6	84	10.4	1.56	5.75	13.6	56.3	NA	5.6	15.7	43	12.8	666	0
Charleston, SC	53.9	75.8	29	95	7.4	2.67	15.00	0.0	—	70	11.0	11.2	49	9.8	66	63
Charleston, WV	42.8	66.8	18	96	13.9	3.31	7.15	0.3	20.7	NA	5.8	16.5	49	7.8	312	6
Charlotte, NC	47.5	71.2	24	96	8.9	2.68	9.01	0.0	3.5	69	9.6	11.6	47	8.8	183	15
Chicago, IL	38.6	58.6	7	91	12.7	3.64	8.33	2.1	13.6	49	6.2	16.2	55	12.1	492	0
Cincinnati, OH	42.2	64.2	15	90	12.8	3.75	9.77	0.4	5.5	40	5.5	16.9	54	10.8	354	0
Cleveland, OH	37.3	57.9	10	88	14.3	3.14	6.61	2.2	14.5	53	5.2	16.9	56	11.8	522	0
Dallas, TX	54.7	76.3	29	101	8.2	3.50	13.04	0.0	0.1	64	8.6	13.5	53	12.7	75	90
Denver, CO	34.5	61.8	−2	90	8.8	1.71	8.24	9.3	33.8	68	6.8	12.4	35	10.2	504	0
Des Moines, IA	40.0	61.8	9	93	10.5	3.36	7.76	2.2	15.6	55	6.9	15.2	54	13.0	428	5
Detroit, MI	36.8	57.7	8	89	12.6	2.95	6.89	1.8	25.7	54	6.5	16.5	55	11.7	531	0
El Paso, TX	48.0	78.7	23	98	1.7	0.20	2.24	0.4	16.5	87	16.5	5.5	16	11.4	110	62
Ely, NV	26.0	57.0	−5	82	7.5	1.00	3.41	6.4	24.5	69	7.7	13.4	34	10.9	705	0
Grand Rapids, MI	35.4	56.6	3	90	13.2	3.37	8.29	3.3	15.6	51	6.5	16.6	57	11.0	570	0
Hartford, CT	37.5	59.9	9	96	11.0	3.85	9.90	1.8	14.3	56	6.5	14.8	52	10.1	489	0
Helena, MT	30.6	56.1	−10	86	8.1	0.97	3.00	4.9	21.7	58	3.8	17.5	38	9.3	648	0
Honolulu, HI	68.7	82.8	57	91	9.4	1.54	12.65	0.0	—	66	5.5	10.6	57	12.1	0	324
Houston, TX	58.1	78.4	31	95	7.0	3.21	10.92	0.0	—	51	7.3	16.2	59	9.4	36	135
Indianapolis, IN	41.5	63.3	16	90	12.3	3.70	8.60	0.5	6.9	54	5.9	16.7	58	11.3	378	0
Jackson, MS	51.9	77.4	30	94	8.8	5.57	15.95	T	T	63	9.1	13.6	59	8.5	87	75
Jacksonville, FL	54.9	79.1	34	95	6.6	2.77	11.61	0.0	—	71	10.1	9.5	65	8.8	37	97
Kansas City, MO	43.8	65.1	12	95	11.3	3.12	10.57	0.8	7.2	64	8.3	15.5	55	12.6	325	10
Las Vegas, NV	50.7	77.5	31	99	1.8	0.21	2.44	T	T	87	16.5	5.9	15	11.0	143	116
Lexington, KY	44.2	65.5	15	91	12.6	3.88	9.30	0.2	5.9	NA	6.2	15.4	55	11.0	312	6
Lincoln, NE	38.9	64.4	3	97	9.9	2.76	9.10	1.3	11.1	59	8.1	14.1	54	12.7	399	0
Little Rock, AR	52.2	72.9	28	95	10.3	5.08	14.81	T	T	62	8.7	13.8	56	9.2	130	58
Los Angeles, CA	54.2	72.3	36	106	3.5	1.03	7.53	0.0	—	70	11.6	9.4	60	8.5	128	77
Lubbock, TX	46.7	75.4	18	100	4.5	0.97	6.18	.02	5.3	74	12.8	8.9	32	14.9	161	44
Marquette, MI	27.0	47.5	−9	92	12.3	2.64	6.80	8.5	43.4	51	NA	NA	NA	NA	831	0
Medford, OR	38.0	64.6	21	96	9.2	1.16	4.40	0.2	4.2	NA	5.9	15.6	45	5.7	416	0
Memphis, TN	52.4	73.3	27	94	10.4	5.46	17.13	T	T	64	8.8	14.2	54	10.7	127	64
Miami, FL	67.8	82.4	46	96	6.0	2.85	17.29	0.0	—	79	8.3	6.9	55	10.6	0	306

	TEMPERATURE (°F) AVERAGE MIN	MAX	RECORD MIN	MAX	MEAN DAYS OF PRECIP	AMOUNT OF PRECIPITATION TOTAL AVG	MAX	SNOWFALL AVG	MAX	% OF POSSIBLE SUN	MEAN CLEAR DAYS	CLOUDY DAYS	REL HUMIDITY	AVG WIND SPEED (MPH)	DEGREE DAYS (BASE 65°F) HEATING	COOLING
Milwaukee, WI	35.8	52.9	12	82	12.0	3.50	7.31	1.9	15.8	53	6.5	15.6	62	13.0	618	0
Minneapolis, MN	36.2	56.5	2	95	10.2	2.42	7.00	3.2	21.8	56	6.8	15.3	52	12.3	558	0
Montgomery, AL	52.9	76.4	28	92	8.2	4.49	15.94	0.0	0.8	65	9.6	12.3	56	7.4	78	69
Nashville, TN	47.5	70.8	23	91	10.9	4.37	11.84	T	1.5	58	8.2	13.3	51	9.4	193	19
New Orleans, LA	58.4	78.5	32	92	7.1	4.50	16.12	0.0	—	63	7.8	11.4	60	9.5	28	133
New York, NY	43.8	61.2	12	96	10.6	4.20	11.51	0.9	13.5	59	7.6	11.9	51	10.5	375	0
Norfolk, VA	47.1	66.9	20	97	9.9	3.06	8.33	T	3.9	65	8.9	11.8	60	11.8	249	9
Oklahoma City, OK	48.8	71.9	20	100	7.8	2.77	11.91	T	4.1	66	9.5	12.7	49	14.5	176	38
Orlando, FL	59.4	83.0	38	96	8.5	1.80	9.10	0.0	—	NA	8.9	8.8	49	8.8	5	191
Philadelphia, PA	42.1	62.6	14	95	10.8	3.62	9.76	0.3	19.4	56	7.1	14.1	48	11.0	378	0
Phoenix, AZ	53.0	83.1	32	105	1.8	0.27	3.36	T	T	88	17.4	5.5	16	7.0	52	142
Pittsburgh, PA	38.8	60.3	11	90	13.4	3.15	8.11	1.4	13.5	48	4.5	17.5	50	10.5	462	0
Portland, OR	41.3	60.6	28	87	14.1	2.39	7.88	T	5.2	52	3.8	20.4	55	7.3	420	0
Providence, RI	37.7	57.0	11	98	10.9	4.11	12.74	0.8	18.0	57	7.9	13.8	58	12.2	528	0
Raleigh, NC	46.2	71.7	23	95	8.7	2.59	7.95	T	5.2	52	3.8	20.4	55	7.3	193	13
Reno, NV	33.3	63.7	13	89	4.1	0.38	3.00	1.4	12.7	80	8.8	11.1	28	8.2	492	0
Sacramento, CA	45.5	71.1	32	98	5.6	1.16	14.20	0.0	T	81	12.5	8.2	43	8.9	230	29
Salt Lake City, UT	37.9	61.3	14	86	9.6	2.12	4.90	5.3	26.4	67	7.0	13.8	39	9.5	464	0
San Antonio, TX	58.4	80.3	31	101	7.4	2.50	11.64	0.0	—	55	7.3	15.3	51	10.6	32	161
San Diego, CA	55.6	68.4	39	98	4.8	0.79	5.37	0.0	—	67	10.3	9.6	58	7.8	113	23
San Francisco, CA	49.8	62.1	31	92	6.0	1.29	10.06	0.0	—	73	11.2	9.6	60	12.1	275	0
Seattle, WA	41.2	57.2	29	87	13.9	2.33	6.53	0.1	2.4	53	2.8	19.9	57	9.6	474	0
Sioux Falls, SD	34.8	59.0	4	94	9.2	2.52	6.97	2.2	18.4	NA	6.9	14.9	53	13.3	543	0
Spokane, WA	34.7	57.0	14	90	8.5	1.18	3.97	0.7	6.6	60	4.5	17.2	44	9.9	573	0
St. Louis, MO	46.4	66.9	20	93	11.4	3.50	10.84	0.4	6.5	56	7.0	14.9	54	11.5	266	17
Tampa, FL	60.8	81.7	38	93	4.7	1.15	10.71	0.0	—	75	10.9	8.0	51	9.5	7	193
Washington, DC	46.4	66.7	15	95	9.8	2.71	9.13	0.0	5.0	58	7.1	14.0	47	10.5	264	9
Wichita, KS	44.5	68.3	15	98	8.0	2.38	12.42	0.3	6.5	63	8.7	13.3	50	14.2	278	20

INTERNATIONAL DATA

	AVG HIGH TEMP	AVG LOW TEMP	AVG PRECIP	DAYS WITH MEASURABLE PRECIP		AVG HIGH TEMP	AVG LOW TEMP	AVG PRECIP	DAYS WITH MEASURABLE PRECIP
Cape Town, South Africa	72	53	1.9	NA	Nairobi, Kenya	79	59	6.0	16
Delhi, India	97	68	0.3	NA	Paris, France	60	43	1.7	13
Hong Kong, China	75	67	5.4	NA	Rio de Janeiro, Brazil	80	69	4.2	10
Jerusalem, Israel	73	50	1.1	NA	Rome, Italy	66	50	2.0	6
London, United Kingdom	56	42	1.5	12	Sydney, Australia	72	58	5.0	13
Manila, Philippines	94	74	0.8	3	Tahiti, Society Islands	89	72	5.6	NA
Melbourne, Australia	68	51	2.3	11	Tokyo, Japan	63	46	5.3	11
Montreal, Canada	51	33	2.9	12	Toronto, Canada	53	33	2.8	11
Moscow, Russia	49	36	1.4	8					

MAY—U.S. CLIMATIC DATA

CITY	TEMPERATURE (°F) AVERAGE MIN	AVERAGE MAX	RECORD MIN	RECORD MAX	MEAN DAYS OF PRECIP	TOTAL AVG	TOTAL MAX	SNOWFALL AVG	SNOWFALL MAX	% OF POSSIBLE SUN	MEAN CLEAR DAYS	MEAN CLOUDY DAYS	REL HUMIDITY	AVG WIND SPEED (MPH)	DEGREE DAYS HEATING	DEGREE DAYS COOLING
Albany, NY	45.4	69.7	26	97	13.1	3.41	8.96	0.1	5.4	55	5.2	16.6	60	9.0	247	18
Albuquerque, NM	48.6	79.7	28	98	4.2	0.50	3.56	0.0	2.0	80	14.8	6.1	18	10.6	89	64
Amarillo, TX	51.6	79.1	26	103	8.3	2.48	9.81	T	9.1	72	11.0	9.6	42	14.6	89	102
Anchorage, AK	38.8	54.4	1	82	6.7	0.73	2.00	0.5	8.8	52	3.9	20.4	49	8.3	570	0
Atlanta, GA	58.7	79.6	37	97	9.1	4.29	9.94	0.0	—	68	9.2	11.4	54	8.6	27	157
Atlantic City, NJ	49.6	71.2	25	99	10.4	3.33	11.51	T	T	54	6.4	14.0	69	10.4	167	25
Bakersfield, CA	57.3	84.6	34	110	1.6	0.20	2.99	0.0	—	NA	18.3	4.2	25	7.9	28	214
Bismarck, ND	42.2	67.8	13	102	9.8	2.18	7.04	0.9	10.3	62	6.2	14.3	44	11.8	324	14
Boise, ID	43.9	71.0	22	99	8.0	1.08	4.90	0.1	4.0	71	8.5	12.5	34	9.5	242	9
Boston, MA	49.8	66.6	31	97	11.7	3.25	13.38	0.0	0.5	59	6.5	14.5	59	12.1	221	10
Buffalo, NY	47.0	66.1	25	94	12.5	3.14	7.35	0.1	5.2	58	5.6	15.8	56	11.5	279	19
Burlington, VT	45.4	67.2	24	93	13.4	3.12	7.10	0.2	3.9	55	5.0	17.0	57	8.8	282	13
Caribou, ME	40.1	61.7	18	96	13.4	3.07	6.27	0.8	10.9	NA	4.0	18.0	61	11.4	437	0
Casper, WY	37.9	66.6	16	95	11.0	2.13	6.46	4.2	32.8	NA	5.1	15.1	41	11.6	394	0
Charleston, SC	62.9	82.7	36	99	9.2	4.01	9.56	0.0	—	71	7.9	12.2	54	8.7	0	242
Charleston, WV	51.5	75.5	26	98	13.2	3.94	8.76	T	0.2	NA	5.8	15.0	55	6.2	129	83
Charlotte, NC	56.4	78.3	32	100	9.7	3.82	12.48	0.0	—	69	8.0	13.1	53	7.6	42	116
Chicago, IL	47.7	70.1	24	98	11.0	3.32	7.59	0.1	2.2	56	7.0	14.0	54	10.5	235	46
Cincinnati, OH	51.8	74.0	27	95	11.5	4.28	9.52	T	1.5	51	5.9	15.6	55	8.8	151	86
Cleveland, OH	47.3	68.6	25	92	13.0	3.49	9.14	0.1	2.1	58	6.0	15.0	57	10.2	250	33
Dallas, TX	62.6	82.9	41	103	8.7	4.88	13.66	0.0	—	64	8.3	11.8	57	11.1	0	246
Denver, CO	43.6	70.8	19	96	10.7	2.40	8.57	1.9	15.5	64	6.0	12.8	38	9.4	253	11
Des Moines, IA	51.5	73.0	26	105	11.2	3.66	11.08	T	1.3	61	7.4	15.1	52	11.3	165	81
Detroit, MI	47.1	69.6	25	95	11.2	2.92	8.46	T	6.0	60	6.3	14.0	53	10.1	243	38
El Paso, TX	56.5	87.1	31	105	2.1	0.25	4.22	0.0	—	89	18.8	4.3	16	10.6	7	217
Ely, NV	33.7	67.3	7	89	7.1	1.15	3.26	2.5	12.1	72	7.7	11.9	31	10.7	450	0
Grand Rapids, MI	45.6	69.3	21	98	10.8	3.13	10.01	T	5.5	54	6.5	15.1	53	9.6	273	40
Hartford, CT	47.6	71.6	28	97	11.5	4.12	12.00	T	1.3	58	5.3	15.8	56	8.9	194	27
Helena, MT	39.6	65.4	17	95	11.1	1.78	6.67	1.5	13.9	50	4.7	16.5	38	8.9	388	
Honolulu, HI	70.3	84.7	60	92	7.3	1.13	7.23	0.0	—	68	6.5	94	54	12.1	0	388
Houston, TX	64.4	84.6	44	99	8.4	5.24	16.88	0.0	—	57	7.0	13.4	50	8.3	0	295
Indianapolis, IN	51.7	73.8	28	96	12.3	4.00	10.10	T	2.4	60	7.1	14.9	57	9.5	165	96
Jackson, MS	60.0	84.0	38	100	9.3	5.05	12.23	0.0	—	63	8.7	11.6	60	7.2	7	224
Jacksonville, FL	62.1	84.7	45	100	8.3	2.55	14.80	0.0	—	69	9.3	9.8	66	8.2	0	260
Kansas City, MO	53.9	74.3	27	103	11.4	5.04	12.75	T	1.7	64	7.5	14.6	58	10.2	135	107
Las Vegas, NV	60.2	87.8	38	109	1.4	0.28	0.96	0.0	—	88	18.6	4.7	13	10.9	14	293
Lexington, KY	53.5	74.3	26	96	11.9	4.47	10.91	0.0	6.0	66	7.2	13.6	56	9.0	135	104
Lincoln, NE	50.0	74.2	25	104	11.2	3.90	11.33	0.1	3.0	62	8.0	13.0	55	10.5	161	72
Little Rock, AR	59.7	79.6	39	98	10.0	5.24	15.91	0.0	—	68	8.0	12.3	59	7.8	31	177
Los Angeles, CA	57.7	73.9	40	103	1.2	0.19	3.57	0.0	—	66	10.1	10.2	66	8.3	72	97
Lubbock, TX	55.8	83.1	29	109	7.4	2.35	7.80	0.0	0.0	73	11.3	8.4	36	14.1	25	162
Marquette, MI	38.4	61.9	17	100	10.4	3.03	8.09	1.5	22.6	57	NA	NA	NA	NA	471	13
Medford, OR	43.4	72.9	28	103	8.1	1.00	4.58	T	T	NA	9.3	12.8	39	5.7	219	8
Memphis, TN	61.2	81.0	38	99	9.2	4.98	13.34	0.0	—	69	8.7	12.6	55	8.9	25	217
Miami, FL	72.1	85.3	50	96	10.4	6.21	18.66	0.0	—	70	5.9	10.0	60	9.5	0	425
Milwaukee, WI	44.8	64.3	21	103	12.0	2.84	9.05	0.0	3.2	59	7.0	14.0	60	11.7	338	16
Minneapolis, MN	47.6	69.4	18	106	11.3	3.39	10.33	0.2	3.0	60	7.0	14.8	50	11.2	244	43
Montgomery, AL	60.8	82.9	40	99	8.5	3.92	12.01	0.0	—	65	9.2	11.6	60	6.2	6	220
Nashville, TN	56.6	78.8	34	97	10.7	4.88	11.04	0.0	T	60	8.3	12.9	56	7.6	59	143
New Orleans, LA	65.2	84.4	41	97	7.6	4.56	21.18	0.0	—	61	9.6	10.2	60	8.1	0	304
New York, NY	53.7	71.7	32	99	11.1	4.42	9.74	T	T	61	8.0	10.7	53	8.8	125	54
Norfolk, VA	56.8	75.3	32	100	9.9	3.81	10.12	0.0	T	65	7.9	13.4	66	10.4	51	85
Oklahoma City, OK	57.7	79.1	32	104	10.0	5.22	12.07	0.0	—	67	8.9	12.2	54	12.7	31	136
Orlando, FL	65.9	87.8	48	102	5.4	3.55	10.36	0.0	—	NA	10.2	8.3	46	9.4	0	369
Philadelphia, PA	52.7	73.1	28	97	11.4	3.75	9.46	T	T	56	6.1	14.4	53	9.6	123	58
Phoenix, AZ	61.5	92.4	39	114	0.9	0.14	1.31	0.0	—	93	21.3	3.5	13	7.0	0	376
Pittsburgh, PA	48.4	70.6	26	95	12.4	3.59	6.56	0.2	3.1	52	5.2	16.6	57	9.0	214	44
Portland, OR	47.0	67.1	29	100	11.7	2.06	6.60	0.0	0.6	58	4.8	18.9	53	7.0	249	0
Providence, RI	47.3	67.3	29	95	11.4	3.76	9.25	0.2	7.0	57	6.7	14.3	63	10.9	246	7
Raleigh, NC	55.3	78.6	31	99	10.3	3.92	9.90	0.0	T	60	8.2	12.7	54	7.7	47	109
Reno, NV	40.1	72.9	16	98	4.3	0.69	2.89	1.0	14.1	82	12.1	9.1	25	7.9	274	10
Sacramento, CA	50.3	80.3	36	107	2.7	0.27	3.25	0.0	—	88	17.8	5.2	35	9.3	80	29
Salt Lake City, UT	45.6	71.9	25	99	8.0	1.80	5.76	0.7	7.5	72	9.2	11.4	33	9.4	215	23
San Antonio, TX	65.7	85.3	43	104	8.3	4.22	14.07	0.0	—	56	6.2	13.6	55	10.2	0	326
San Diego, CA	59.1	69.1	45	98	2.3	0.19	2.54	0.0	—	58	8.6	11.1	64	7.8	73	45
San Francisco, CA	50.5	62.7	36	106	2.7	0.25	4.02	0.0	—	72	13.9	7.5	60	13.3	260	0
Seattle, WA	46.3	63.9	28	93	10.2	1.70	4.76	T	T	56	4.4	17.5	54	9.0	307	0
Sioux Falls, SD	45.9	70.7	17	104	10.4	3.03	9.42	T	3.0	NA	7.3	13.8	49	11.9	240	35
Spokane, WA	41.9	65.8	24	97	9.2	1.41	3.97	0.1	3.5	63	5.6	15.0	41	9.0	344	0
St. Louis, MO	56.0	76.1	31	96	10.8	3.97	12.92	T	4.0	61	7.6	13.8	56	9.5	111	145
Tampa, FL	67.5	87.2	49	98	6.4	3.10	17.64	0.0	—	75	10.2	8.7	53	8.9	0	378
Washington, DC	56.6	76.2	28	99	11.2	3.66	10.69	T	T	59	7.3	13.8	52	9.2	60	104
Wichita, KS	54.3	76.9	27	100	10.6	3.81	11.22	0.0	—	65	8.3	12.7	54	12.5	102	121

INTERNATIONAL DATA

CITY	AVG HIGH TEMP	AVG LOW TEMP	AVG PRECIP	DAYS WITH MEASURABLE PRECIP
Cape Town, South Africa	67	49	3.7	NA
Delhi, India	105	79	0.5	NA
Hong Kong, China	82	74	11.5	NA
Jerusalem, Israel	81	57	0.1	NA
London, United Kingdom	62	47	1.8	12
Manila, Philippines	94	76	4.0	8
Melbourne, Australia	62	47	2.2	14
Montreal, Canada	65	45	2.6	12
Moscow, Russia	63	48	2.1	6
Nairobi, Kenya	76	58	5.0	14
Paris, France	67	49	2.2	12
Rio de Janeiro, Brazil	77	66	3.1	10
Rome, Italy	74	56	1.8	5
Sydney, Australia	67	52	4.8	13
Tahiti, Society Islands	87	70	4.0	NA
Tokyo, Japan	71	54	5.8	12
Toronto, Canada	65	43	2.6	11

JUNE—U.S. CLIMATIC DATA

City	TEMPERATURE (°F) AVERAGE MIN	AVERAGE MAX	RECORD MIN	RECORD MAX	MEAN DAYS OF PRECIP	PRECIP TOTAL AVG	TOTAL MAX	SNOWFALL AVG	SNOWFALL MAX	% OF POSSIBLE SUN	CLEAR DAYS	CLOUDY DAYS	REL HUMIDITY	AVG WIND SPEED (MPH)	DEGREE DAYS HEATING	COOLING
Albany, NY	54.6	79.0	35	100	11.2	3.62	8.74	0.0	—	59	5.3	13.6	64	8.2	34	91
Albuquerque, NM	58.3	90.0	40	107	3.7	0.59	8.15	0.0	—	83	17.9	3.5	17	10.0	0	279
Amarillo, TX	60.7	87.6	38	108	8.3	3.70	10.73	0.0	0.3	77	13.0	5.8	44	14.3	6	279
Anchorage, AK	47.2	61.6	29	86	8.4	1.14	3.40	0.0	0.4	48	2.5	20.5	55	8.2	318	0
Atlanta, GA	66.2	85.8	39	102	9.9	3.56	11.21	0.0	—	67	7.6	10.2	57	8.0	0	330
Atlantic City, NJ	58.7	80.0	37	106	8.9	2.64	8.45	0.0	—	58	6.9	12.1	71	9.3	12	144
Bakersfield, CA	64.0	92.4	38	114	0.5	0.10	1.11	0.0	—	NA	23.5	1.9	23	7.9	6	402
Bismarck, ND	51.6	77.1	30	111	11.8	2.72	9.90	0.0	2.0	64	7.4	12.2	48	10.5	116	98
Boise, ID	52.1	80.9	30	109	6.4	0.81	3.41	T	T	75	11.5	8.3	30	9.1	75	120
Boston, MA	59.1	76.3	41	100	10.5	3.09	13.20	0.0	—	64	6.9	12.6	59	11.3	32	113
Buffalo, NY	56.5	75.3	35	97	10.3	3.55	9.67	T	T	65	6.3	12.2	57	11.0	59	86
Burlington, VT	54.6	75.8	33	100	12.5	3.47	9.92	0.0	—	58	4.8	14.6	62	8.3	58	64
Caribou, ME	49.1	71.9	30	96	13.6	2.91	7.11	T	T	NA	3.3	16.9	65	10.4	143	8
Casper, WY	46.9	78.6	28	102	8.5	1.46	4.71	0.2	4.5	NA	9.6	9.6	33	11.0	139	70
Charleston, SC	69.1	87.6	49	104	10.8	6.43	27.24	0.0	—	68	6.2	12.5	59	8.3	0	399
Charleston, WV	59.8	83.1	33	105	11.3	3.59	10.67	0.0	—	NA	4.7	12.2	61	5.6	10	202
Charlotte, NC	65.6	85.8	45	103	9.8	3.39	11.04	0.0	—	70	7.4	11.5	57	6.9	0	32
Chicago, IL	57.5	79.6	35	104	10.3	3.78	10.58	0.0	T	67	7.3	11.3	55	9.1	35	143
Cincinnati, OH	60.0	82.0	39	102	10.5	3.84	9.86	0.0	—	73	6.9	12.8	56	7.9	11	191
Cleveland, OH	56.8	78.3	31	104	11.0	3.70	10.73	0.0	—	65	6.7	12.0	58	9.4	40	118
Dallas, TX	70.0	91.9	51	113	5.9	2.98	12.18	0.0	—	71	11.3	7.3	50	10.8	0	480
Denver, CO	52.4	81.4	30	104	8.9	1.79	4.96	0.0	0.4	71	9.6	8.1	35	8.9	71	128
Des Moines, IA	61.2	82.2	37	103	10.8	4.46	15.71	0.0	—	68	8.1	11.4	53	10.3	10	214
Detroit, MI	56.3	78.9	36	104	10.5	3.61	8.31	0.0	—	66	7.8	11.1	54	9.0	38	116
El Paso, TX	64.3	96.5	46	114	3.3	0.67	3.18	0.0	—	89	20.0	2.8	18	9.5	0	462
Ely, NV	40.7	78.3	18	99	4.8	0.88	3.53	.02	5.6	80	13.3	6.5	23	10.6	188	26
Grand Rapids, MI	55.3	78.7	32	102	10.2	3.68	13.22	0.0	—	61	6.4	12.3	56	8.8	50	110
Hartford, CT	56.9	80.0	37	100	11.3	3.75	13.60	0.0	—	60	5.5	14.0	60	8.1	20	125
Helena, MT	48.3	75.8	30	102	11.7	1.87	5.63	0.1	2.7	62	5.6	13.4	38	8.6	137	50
Honolulu, HI	72.2	86.5	64	92	6.0	0.50	4.26	0.0	—	70	5.5	7.1	53	12.8	0	432
Houston, TX	70.6	90.1	52	103	7.9	4.96	19.21	0.0	—	64	9.1	8.8	59	7.7	0	462
Indianapolis, IN	37.0	82.7	39	102	10.0	3.49	12.21	0.0	—	66	7.0	12.3	58	8.5	5	212
Jackson, MS	67.1	90.6	47	105	8.0	3.18	9.69	0.0	—	70	9.7	8.4	60	6.3	0	414
Jacksonville, FL	69.1	89.3	47	103	12.0	5.69	23.32	0.0	—	63	5.7	11.2	73	8.0	0	423
Kansas City, MO	63.1	83.3	42	108	10.2	4.72	11.86	0.0	—	69	9.6	10.8	58	9.9	7	253
Las Vegas, NV	69.4	100.3	48	116	0.7	0.12	0.97	0.0	—	92	22.4	2.5	10	11.0	0	597
Lexington, KY	61.5	82.7	39	104	10.7	3.66	11.69	0.0	—	NA	7.4	11.3	57	8.1	5	221
Lincoln, NE	60.2	84.7	39	109	7.9	3.89	12.93	0.0	—	70	9.7	10.4	51	10.1	11	236
Little Rock, AR	67.5	87.4	46	105	8.1	3.26	9.28	0.0	—	73	9.5	8.9	57	7.4	0	375
Los Angeles, CA	61.1	78.3	46	112	0.5	0.03	1.39	0.0	—	65	9.3	9.6	67	7.9	35	176
Lubbock, TX	64.3	90.0	49	114	7.0	2.76	8.48	0.0	0.0	77	13.5	5.6	37	11.2	0	366
Marquette, MI	47.4	70.9	25	101	12.3	3.48	6.61	T	0.2	58	NA	NA	NA	NA	193	19
Medford, OR	50.7	82.1	31	111	5.3	0.58	3.49	0.0	T	NA	12.6	9.2	33	5.9	60	105
Memphis, TN	68.9	89.3	48	104	8.4	3.57	18.16	0.0	—	74	10.1	8.8	56	8.0	0	423
Miami, FL	75.1	87.6	60	98	15.0	9.33	25.34	0.0	—	75	3.3	12.5	66	8.2	0	492
Milwaukee, WI	55.0	74.9	33	104	11.1	3.24	10.03	0.0	—	64	7.7	12.1	61	10.5	82	82
Minneapolis, MN	57.6	78.8	34	104	12.0	4.05	9.00	0.0	—	64	7.5	12.4	53	10.5	41	137
Montgomery, AL	67.9	89.4	48	106	9.0	3.90	15.59	0.0	—	65	8.6	9.9	59	5.9	0	411
Nashville, TN	64.7	86.5	42	106	9.4	3.57	11.95	0.0	—	66	8.3	9.4	55	7.0	0	318
New Orleans, LA	70.8	89.2	50	102	10.2	5.84	17.62	0.0	—	67	9.4	7.9	62	6.8	0	450
New York, NY	63.0	80.1	44	101	10.1	3.67	10.27	0.0	—	64	8.0	9.6	55	8.1	0	203
Norfolk, VA	65.2	82.9	40	104	9.0	3.82	10.53	0.0	—	68	7.6	10.8	67	9.6	0	277
Oklahoma City, OK	66.1	87.3	46	107	8.5	4.31	14.76	0.0	—	74	10.8	8.6	54	12.3	0	351
Orlando, FL	71.8	90.5	53	100	13.8	7.32	18.28	0.0	—	NA	4.5	11.4	57	8.0	0	483
Philadelphia, PA	61.8	81.7	44	102	10.3	3.74	10.06	0.0	—	62	7.0	11.8	54	8.7	5	209
Phoenix, AZ	70.6	102.3	49	122	0.7	0.17	1.70	0.0	—	94	23.3	2.2	12	6.9	0	645
Pittsburgh, PA	56.9	78.9	34	98	11.3	3.71	10.29	0.0	—	57	5.3	13.2	52	8.0	36	123
Portland, OR	52.9	74.0	39	102	9.6	1.48	5.38	T	T	55	5.9	16.7	49	7.1	91	46
Providence, RI	56.8	76.9	39	101	10.8	3.33	11.08	0.0	—	60	6.9	12.8	67	10.0	31	88
Raleigh, NC	63.6	85.0	38	104	9.2	3.68	10.44	0.0	—	61	7.6	10.5	56	7.0	0	279
Reno, NV	46.9	83.1	25	103	3.1	0.46	1.94	T	0.2	85	16.8	5.6	22	7.5	76	79
Sacramento, CA	55.3	87.8	41	115	1.1	0.12	1.45	0.0	—	93	21.7	2.5	31	9.8	12	210
Salt Lake City, UT	55.4	82.8	32	104	5.6	0.93	3.84	T	2.0	79	13.6	6.3	26	9.4	51	174
San Antonio, TX	72.6	91.8	48	107	5.9	3.81	11.95	0.0	—	67	7.0	7.6	51	10.2	0	516
San Diego, CA	61.9	71.6	50	101	1.0	0.07	0.87	0.0	—	57	9.1	9.1	66	7.7	51	105
San Francisco, CA	52.6	64.1	41	106	1.1	0.15	2.57	0.0	—	73	16.1	5.3	59	13.9	198	0
Seattle, WA	51.9	69.9	38	100	9.3	1.50	3.90	0.0	—	54	4.9	17.4	53	8.7	144	21
Sioux Falls, SD	56.1	80.5	32	110	10.9	3.40	8.43	0.0	—	NA	8.6	10.3	51	10.7	50	149
Spokane, WA	49.2	74.7	33	101	7.8	1.26	5.12	T	T	66	7.2	12.4	36	9.0	139	49
St. Louis, MO	65.7	85.2	43	104	9.4	3.72	12.35	0.0	T	66	7.4	11.7	56	8.8	0	312
Tampa, FL	72.9	89.5	53	99	11.6	5.48	18.52	0.0	—	67	5.4	10.6	50	8.2	0	480
Washington, DC	66.5	84.7	36	102	9.4	3.38	18.19	0.0	—	65	7.9	11.3	53	8.7	0	318
Wichita, KS	64.6	86.8	43	110	9.3	4.31	14.43	0.0	—	69	9.6	9.9	49	12.2	5	326

INTERNATIONAL DATA

City	AVG HIGH TEMP	AVG LOW TEMP	AVG PRECIP	DAYS WITH MEASURABLE PRECIP	City	AVG HIGH TEMP	AVG LOW TEMP	AVG PRECIP	DAYS WITH MEASURABLE PRECIP
Cape Town, South Africa	65	46	4.3	NA	Nairobi, Kenya	75	54	1.3	5
Delhi, India	102	83	2.9	NA	Paris, France	73	55	2.1	12
Hong Kong, China	85	78	15.5	NA	Rio de Janeiro, Brazil	76	64	2.1	7
Jerusalem, Israel	85	60	0	NA	Rome, Italy	82	63	1.5	4
London, United Kingdom	69	53	1.8	11	Sydney, Australia	62	48	5.2	12
Manila, Philippines	91	75	10.1	16	Tahiti, Society Islands	86	69	3.0	NA
Melbourne, Australia	57	44	2.0	14	Tokyo, Japan	76	63	6.5	12
Montreal, Canada	75	55	3.2	12	Toronto, Canada	75	53	2.6	9
Moscow, Russia	69	53	2.6	7					

For Kim
from Auntie
Xmas 2010
Much love

FRANK LLOYD WRIGHT

Constantin Bran
The essence

FRANK LLOYD WRIGHT

Quercus

A NEW BEGINNING

THE LATER WORKS

THE LEGACY OF FRANK LLOYD WRIGHT

INDEX

THE LIFE OF FRANK LLOYD WRIGHT

FRANK LLOYD WRIGHT, who has strong claims to be considered North America's greatest architect, lived from 1867 to 1959. His life therefore began in the steam age and ended in the space age. When he was born, American architecture was drawing on a range of styles, some based on the architecture of medieval Europe, some on more recent examples from France. By the time he died, a new, distinctive kind of architecture had evolved, responsive to the needs of people living both in the cities and in the open spaces of the USA. Frank Lloyd Wright was one of the most important creators of this new architecture, as well as the designer of some of North America's most beautiful and memorable buildings.

Frank Lloyd Wright was born in 1867 in the town of Richland Center, Wisconsin. His parents were William Carey Wright, a preacher and musician, and Anna Lloyd Jones Wright, a schoolteacher who was 14 years younger than her husband. William Wright had various short-term jobs preaching and giving music lessons, but found it hard to find permanent employment, so when Frank was young the family moved several times as William looked for work. His mother was a more rooted personality. She came from a family of Welsh religious dissenters who had arrived in the USA in 1844. Independent-minded, strongly religious and immersed in the culture of Transcendentalism that was so strong in the USA in the 19th century, Anna was to have the more enduring influence on her son.

An architect's education

When he was a boy, Wright was educated by his mother, who started a small school run on the principles established by the German educationalist Friedrich Froebel. The Froebel system stressed learning from nature and fostered spatial awareness. This educational system promoted analytical thinking by encouraging children to take objects apart and reassemble them, and emphasized the patterns and geometries that lay behind the things that made up the physical world. In addition, Froebel stressed the spiritual side of life – helping to show that the spiritual and material spheres were actually aspects of the same world. With its emphasis on design, spatial awareness and analysis, a Froebel education was a good one for an architect.

In the early 1880s, William and Anna's marriage began to fall apart and in 1884 the couple divorced. Frank, their eldest child and only son, had to go to work to help support his mother and sisters. He joined the office of the engineer Allan Conover in Madison, Wisconsin, where he worked while also studying engineering at the University of Wisconsin. This engineering background stood Wright in good stead when he came to design his own buildings – it was a very American and pragmatic training for an architect, and it helped him when he wanted to push structures in new and challenging directions. Wright's time with Conover was a useful apprenticeship.

Working with Sullivan

But Madison offered limited opportunities for an aspiring architect, so at the age of 20, Wright left for Chicago. Here he worked first in the office of the architect J. Lyman Silsbee and then, after a year, for the prominent Chicago firm of Adler and Sullivan.

Architect Louis Sullivan quickly recognized Wright's abilities, and the young architect was soon a key figure in the office of Adler and Sullivan, who were designing landmark buildings in Chicago and other cities. Working with Sullivan on major structures such as the Wainwright, Schiller and Auditorium

OPPOSITE Frank Lloyd Wright in 1904. Aged 37, he had been in independent practice for just over ten years and had already designed some of his most important early buildings, including the houses for Ward Willits and Susan Lawrence Dana. His first church, Unity Temple in Oak Park, Illinois, was on the drafting table.

ABOVE A group of students at Taliesin, the architect's home and workplace at Spring Green, Wisconsin, gathers around a drafting table to watch Frank Lloyd Wright at work. Whether he was beginning a new drawing from scratch or correcting the work of one of the students, there was always much to learn from watching the master.

Buildings gave Wright experience at the cutting edge of architecture. It also gave him contacts. Soon he was moonlighting – doing designs for his own clients in the evenings while designing in Sullivan's office by day. Wright was later to claim that Sullivan fired him because he took on these unofficial commissions, although there is some doubt about this story.

The year 1893 proved to be a turning point for Wright. At the Chicago International Exposition that year he saw his first Japanese building, the Japanese National Pavilion. With its wooden beams, overhanging roofs and fluid internal spaces, it was to have a huge influence on Wright's architecture. The other pivotal event that year came when Daniel Burnham, probably America's most successful architect at the time, offered to pay for Wright to study classical architecture in Paris and Rome for six years,

followed by a guarantee of a job in Burnham's office. It was a
dream offer, but Wright turned Burnham down. He didn't want to
study the ancient, European conventions of classical architecture.
The young architect stayed in the Midwest to open his own office
and pursue a more modern, more American dream.

Making it new
'Make it new,' said the poet Ezra Pound,
pointing the way forward for the American artist in the 20th
century. The buildings that Wright designed in the years around
the turn of the century saw him developing his own style and
creating a new, essentially American, kind of architecture –
inventive, problem-solving and responsive both to clients' needs
and to the American landscape. This was the period in which
Wright designed the Larkin Company Administration Building in
Buffalo, New York, a groundbreaking office building that provided
comfortable working conditions for some 1,800 workers and
pioneered the use of new technologies such as air conditioning.
Equally revolutionary was Unity Temple, Oak Park, Illinois, the first
church in America to be built of exposed concrete, a material that
Wright had quickly learned to handle beautifully.

Meanwhile, a string of houses in the years leading up to the
First World War saw Wright developing looser plans in which one
living space flowed into the next, in which rooms with generous
windows were sheltered by equally lavish overhanging eaves, and
in which designs were worked out with the individual client's
requirements clearly in mind. Out of this group of designs, Wright
developed what he called the Prairie House. These low-slung,
ground-hugging houses often had cross-shaped footprints, spread
out in all directions to take advantage of the sun's position at
different times of day. With their horizontal profiles, roomy interiors
and the way they are grounded in the landscape, they redefined
the American house.

The Prairie Houses were built for rich clients, people with live-
in servants and the money to build on a big scale; but Wright also
wanted to produce a more 'democratic' architecture. He began to design smaller houses such as the
'Fireproof House for $5,000', which he published in the *Ladies' Home Journal* in 1906. He would return
to such ideas later in his career, looking for new ways to build houses on a tight budget.

Crisis
In 1909, as he came to the end of his sequence of Prairie Houses, a crisis occurred in
Wright's life. He began an affair with Mamah Borthwick Cheney, the wife of a client, and left his wife
Catherine and their six children to visit Europe with Mamah. When Wright returned to the USA he
learned that Catherine would not grant him a divorce, and he set up home with Mamah in a new house,
Taliesin, which he built in Spring Green, Wisconsin. But in 1914 disaster struck: Julian Carlton, a servant
who had been threatened with dismissal, ran amok, set the house on fire and killed several people,
including Mamah.

The following years were difficult ones for Wright. He spent much of the period between 1914 and
1923 in Japan designing Tokyo's Imperial Hotel, returning to North America from time to time to work on
the few other jobs he had – most notably Hollyhock House, the outstanding home that he built in Los
Angeles for oil heiress Aline Barnsdall. The Tokyo hotel was a notable success, especially when Wright's
tremor-resistant construction method was proved to work during the disastrous earthquake of 1923.
But it kept the architect away from the USA for long periods, and his work in North America declined.
However, during his absence in Japan his son Lloyd, also an architect, had found clients in California;
in addition, Wright and Catherine had finally divorced in 1922 and he had married the sculptor Miriam
Noel. He decided to open an office in Los Angeles.

California seemed to offer a new beginning. Wright developed a way of designing houses
constructed of cast concrete blocks, and four of these were built. But Wright's capacity for spending
money was far greater than his income warranted and his emotional life was still in turmoil – Miriam
turned out to be addicted to morphine, and on one occasion threatened Wright with a knife. Scarcely a
year after his marriage to Miriam, Wright found consolation with another woman: he met and fell in love
with Olgivanna Hinzenberg, a Montenegro-born dancer and wife of the Russian architect Valdemar
Hinzenberg. But the architect's troubles were far from over. By 1926 he was deeply in debt and his bank
took possession of Taliesin. Meanwhile, the jealous Miriam pursued Wright, Olgivanna and their baby,
threatening to have Wright arrested for a violation of the Mann Act, a law that targeted traffickers of
immigrant prostitutes.

ABOVE Frank Lloyd Wright
instructs a bulldozer driver at
Spring Green, Wisconsin, in 1945.
The ground is being prepared for
improvements to the architect's
property – probably the
construction of dams to create a
small lake to regulate water flow
through the adjacent farmland.

In 1927 Wright was granted a divorce from Miriam; the following year he married Olgivanna, and the pair tried to sort out their lives. But as the Great Depression struck, architectural work was still harder to come by. With Olgivanna's encouragement, Wright turned to writing and lecturing as a way of both earning a living and publicizing his work and ideas. He published many articles, an *Autobiography* and a book about urban planning, *The Disappearing City*. In addition, he turned Taliesin into a combination of communal settlement, architecture school and architectural practice by inviting people to pay him to serve as his apprentices.

Olgivanna remained central to the life of the Taliesin Fellowship as a self-appointed spiritual leader, adviser and manager second only to Wright himself in importance and influence. She helped to maintain the strictly hierarchical system of the Fellowship (indeed 'Fellowship' was an inappropriate name), in which everyone had to defer to Wright and Olgivanna. The architect was always referred to as 'Mr Wright', and criticism of his ideas was frowned upon.

New directions

The 1930s saw Wright return to his ideas about a more democratic architecture. He began a series of houses for middle-income Americans that were more compact and cheaper to build than his earlier, lavish Prairie Houses. These houses, which Wright called 'Usonian Houses', were usually built on one level and based on a modular design, often using standard components and lots of timber in the structure. They were houses for a modern lifestyle, for people without servants.

The Usonian Houses had an open plan, with the kitchen often placed centrally so that the woman of the house could keep an eye on her children while preparing meals. They lacked the large stable blocks or garages of the Prairie Houses – if the family had an automobile, it could be kept in a carport formed from an overhanging flat roof. The accommodation was designed for people who lived in the machine age, with labour-saving domestic appliances. But they were also meant to keep people in touch with the land, their L-shaped or tadpole-shaped plans opening on to gardens through numerous glazed doors.

Wright designed many variations on the Usonian theme, and this work kept his practice busy in the 1930s, in addition spreading his ideas through a new stratum of American society. At the same time, he took on work for rich clients who admired his ideas of 'organic architecture'. These major houses included Fallingwater (for store owner Edgar J. Kaufmann) and Wingspread (for Herbert Johnson, of the Johnson Wax Company, for whom Wright also designed a notable headquarters building).

The architect continued his writing and proselytizing too. Some of his boldest ideas were embodied in projects that, although they were never built, demonstrated what Wright saw as the way forward for American architecture and urban planning. The greatest example was a project called Broadacre City, an 'ideal' city design that Wright developed and revised at various times during his working life. The key idea behind this concept was that each American family should have one acre (0.4 ha) of land on which to build their house.

The successes of the 1930s and 1940s brought Wright wider recognition, although other architects were slow to follow up his ideas. However, in 1949 Wright was finally presented with the Gold Medal of the American Institute of Architects, showing that his innovative work was at last recognized by his country's architectural establishment.

The late work

Wright continued to design through his eighties, and in the 1950s created several of his most memorable buildings, both large and small. He developed the concept of the Usonian House still further, creating what he called the 'Usonian Automatic', a concrete-block house so easy to build that, in theory at least, much of the construction work could be done by the clients themselves. Wright's last years also saw the designs for major buildings such as New York's Guggenheim Museum and the Beth Sholom Synagogue in Philadelphia. Although some of the late buildings – such as the buildings for Marin County in California – have been seen by some as marking a decline in his powers, structures such as the Guggenheim Museum show that, right up to the end of his life, Wright was capable of highly original designs that explored new architectural directions.

Frank Lloyd Wright died on 9 April 1959, in Phoenix, Arizona. The commitment of his associates and apprentices in the Taliesin Fellowship meant that a number of major projects, including the Guggenheim Museum, still under construction at the time of his death were brought to completion. Among his 500 built structures, some 400 still survive as clear and lasting evidence of the multifaceted genius of America's greatest architect.

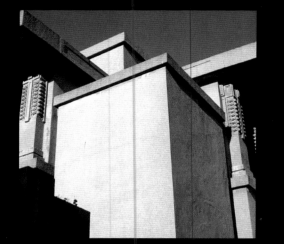

FRANK LLOYD WRIGHT OFTEN FOUND himself going out on a limb, an experience he clearly enjoyed. As a young man he showed no desire to follow the way of life of either his father (a preacher) or his mother's male relatives (who were mostly farmers). He wanted to be an architect, but when he began work in the profession, he found there, too, he was going his own way. As a young architect in the office of Adler and Sullivan, a great practice at the height of their success, he was drawn not to their large public building projects, but to the residential work that did not interest the senior partners. But even here he showed signs that he wanted to design houses that were different from the norm, buildings less reliant on European traditions than those produced by other American architects.

The buildings in this chapter show Wright finding his way as an architect after he left the office of Adler and Sullivan and began to establish his own methods. They see him thinking projects through from the very basics, so that he could create, for example, a radical design for a church (Unity Temple) and a new kind of wind pump (the Romeo and Juliet Windmill). They show how he enthusiastically embraced new materials, as with the poured concrete of Unity Temple. They find him looking in unusual directions for work and inspiration, especially to Japan, for Tokyo's Imperial Hotel. And, most remarkably, they see him embracing new technologies in the air-conditioned, double-glazed Larkin Building.

As his career developed, Wright fused all these elements in an architecture that was unlike anything else, a way of building that was painstakingly thought through rather than being a slavish copy of previous architects or styles. For the first time, Wright claimed, the USA had its own, thoroughly American, kind of architecture.

ROOTS
OF AN
ARCHITECT

Frank Lloyd Wright House

In 1889 the 21-year-old Frank Lloyd Wright fell in love with Catherine Tobin, whom he had met at a social gathering at his church in Oak Park, Chicago. Naturally, when the couple planned to get married, the young architect wanted to build a home for himself and his wife. The building he designed, a compact house dominated by a large, dramatic gable, stands out from its neighbours; but, clad in shingles, the house also uses traditional materials. Like so many of his later buildings, this first house is an enthralling mixture of old and new.

Location
Oak Park, Illinois

Client
The architect

Date
1889

Main materials
Wood, shingle, brick

Wright and Catherine were eager to marry, but the young architect had no job security and no money. He told his boss, Louis Sullivan, about his plans, and Sullivan immediately called in his partner, Dankmar Adler. 'What do you say to a five-year contract?' asked Sullivan. Adler was agreeable and Wright got his security. Emboldened by Sullivan's support, Wright then asked his boss for a loan to build a house for Catherine and himself. Sullivan agreed, advancing Wright $5,000 to buy some land and build a modest house in Oak Park.

Old and new So a year after he began working for Adler and Sullivan, Wright designed his marital home. The new house was Wright's first independent building, and, like so many of his later houses, is a rich mixture of the old and the new. It is a shingle-clad building, the exterior dominated by a huge gable – a bold architectural statement that immediately impresses and makes the building stand out. Shingles were a popular and traditional wall-cladding – there were 'shingle-style' houses all over the USA, especially in the east. But Wright did something quite dramatic and striking with the style. The big sweeping gable and the bold strips of casement windows beneath it owe a lot to the designs of the great British Arts and Crafts architect C.F.A. Voysey, and perhaps something to the Scottish master Charles Rennie Mackintosh. No doubt Wright had been reading the architectural magazines.

RIGHT Leaded windowpanes became one of Wright's hallmarks. In this early house, they are used in a conventional diamond pattern, as they were in many other 19th-century buildings. The architect prized them for the multifaceted way they reflect the light, which is more 'alive' than with large panes of plate glass.

OPPOSITE From the outside, the most striking feature of the Frank Lloyd Wright house is the large gable that sweeps down to first-floor level, casting strong shadows. This gable, together with the building's wings and bays, shows how the young architect was already developing his skill with the handling of shapes and forms.

Larkin Company Administration Building

The Larkin headquarters, an office block for a large company supplying a range of household goods, was one of the great buildings of the early 20th century. The façade was of heavy masonry, relieved only by a pair of tall pillars, but at the side there were big windows to fill the workspaces with light. Inside there was a huge top-lit atrium, surrounded by balconies with scores of desks. This layout was subsequently imitated in countless office buildings, though few of its imitators were as grand and monumental.

Location
Buffalo, New York

Client
Larkin Company

Date
1903 (demolished 1950)

Main material
Brick

OPPOSITE Large masses of masonry gave the street façade of the Larkin Administration Building a monumental quality, which the architect hoped would still look impressive if the walls were blackened by industrial pollution. Although there were some windows in the centre part of the frontage, they gave little hint of how light the building was inside.

RIGHT Skylights illuminated the vast atrium of the building, throwing into relief the carved decoration on the upper parts of the columns. The balcony fronts bore uplifting inscriptions, reminding the Larkin Company's employees of the virtues of such qualities as economy, industry and cooperation.

'Nearly every technological innovation used today was suggested in the Larkin Building in 1904.' Frank Lloyd Wright was rarely modest about his buildings but this time he was not far wrong. The list is staggering: air conditioning, double-glazed plate-glass windows, glass doors, built-in steel desks, hung lavatory walls that you could clean beneath, wall-mounted WCs, a built-in vacuum-cleaning system, sub-floor electric lighting. All these features of the Larkin Building were widely copied by other architects in the following decades.

The Larkin Company had begun in 1875 as a soap manufacturer but by the beginning of the 20th century it had expanded into groceries, furniture and household goods. They sold the goods they made by mail order, cutting out the middleman. The business boomed, and the company needed new offices.

A landmark building
Wright gave them a building to be proud of, a building that made a mark on its Buffalo street, stood out from the huge Larkin factories and warehouses behind it, and provided an efficient and agreeable environment for its workers. This was a combination that appealed to Larkin and his fellow directors, who were happy to invest some of their wealth in a building that would be pleasant for their employees.

Outside, the Larkin Building was like a fortress – a great cliff of a building in dark brick, on five floors. Tall, massive and brooding, this exterior looked somewhat forbidding, but it was also practical. Wright chose the dark brick because he knew that the walls would soon become soiled with city grime, and the dark colour would take the scars of pollution better than paler masonry.

Both light and enlightened
The interior was a rather different story. For a start, it was very light, making it an inviting place in which to work, something that appealed to the Larkin bosses, who valued their workers' welfare. A huge central atrium was topped with a skylight, illuminating the workspaces on the first floor below and on the balconies that lined this huge space. The wall cladding, a cream-coloured glazed brick that could be easily cleaned, increased the lightness. In all, it made a comfortable workplace for the 1,800 administrative workers of the Larkin empire.

This was just as well, because the building went $62,000 over budget. The Larkins were shocked, but soon realized that the landmark headquarters they now had was worth much more than this in publicity value. An illustration of the building was printed on their letterhead, and became an effective symbol of the firm.

The Larkin Company did well until the Great Depression, but, like many, did not recover from the economic disaster. The building was sold in 1943 and demolished in 1950. Now the innovative design of Wright's early masterpiece can be appreciated only through photographs.

Unity Temple

The church where Wright worshipped every Sunday was always a special building to him and he designed it to stand out on the street. At the front of the building, plain walls are pierced by high windows and topped by flat overhanging roofs. At each corner, bulky square stair towers flank the main façades. This is a revolutionary design for a church, all the more so because it is built in poured concrete, an unusual but trendsetting material for a public building in the early 1900s.

In 1905 the Unitarian church in Oak Park was destroyed in a fire. The congregation straight away began to plan a replacement for the old building, which had been an old-fashioned Gothic Revival church. There were two problems. First, just $40,000 was available to pay for the new building. Second, it was difficult to decide what kind of building everyone wanted, and who should design it.

The church and the people

Some members of the congregation wanted to hold a competition to choose the best design, but the building committee that had been formed threw out this idea. The pastor, Dr Rodney F. Johonnot, liked the idea of a traditional North American colonial church, a white building with a spire, but the committee chose Wright as architect and Wright's ideas were a very long way from traditional. He did not like the idea of a spire. 'Why build a conventional church, with a spire pointing literally to heaven?' he said. He preferred instead the notion that God's kingdom was present in the gathering of worshipping people.

Wright planned a church that would look like no previous place of worship, a building that even at over a hundred years old still looks rather surprising in its leafy surroundings. It is a tribute to the congregation – and perhaps the persuasive powers of the architect and his friend on the building committee, Charles E. Roberts – that it got built at all.

Location
Oak Park, Illinois

Client
The congregation
of Unity Church

Date
1905

Main material
Poured concrete

RIGHT This exterior view in strong sunlight shows how the temple's walls resolve into a composition of planes and forms as ordered as a constructivist painting. The flat roofs, slightly projecting cornices and decorative elements are designed to cast shadows in the sun to relieve the effect of the expanses of pale concrete.

LEFT The skylights are glazed with stained glass in simple abstract patterns of rectangles and squares, each square deeply recessed for added shadows and visual textures. The colour of the glass is just strong enough to give a warm glow to the light inside the building.

One challenge of the project was the site, which had a narrow frontage but went back a long way. Wright turned this to his advantage, placing the church, Unity Temple itself, at the front, and building another linked structure, Unity House, at the back to accommodate the lay activities of the congregation.

Unity Temple, like many other churches, is a cruciform structure, but it does not look cross-shaped from the outside because Wright placed at the corners square stair towers that rise almost to the top of the building. These towers combine with the plain walls, high windows and flat roofs to make an astonishing composition for a church, with little ornament except for the ornate uprights in the windows, which have reminded many of the decorations on Mayan temples.

A new use for concrete

What is more, the church is built of concrete, and the walls were made by pouring the concrete on site. This method became commonplace in the later 20th century, but was little short of revolutionary in 1905. Only one or two previous buildings had been constructed in this way, and no one had built a church like this: Unity Temple was America's first public building constructed of exposed concrete. Many contemporaries found the resulting wall surfaces ugly. As Wright's biographer Brendan Gill puts it, 'Many parishioners prayed for ivy and were happy when ivy came.'

ABOVE By running red and black lines around many elements – pulpit, light fittings and balcony fronts as well as walls – Wright brought a formal unity to the interior of the church. In a space without lavish images or rich decoration, Wright created a peaceful atmosphere that fosters contemplation, reading and prayer.

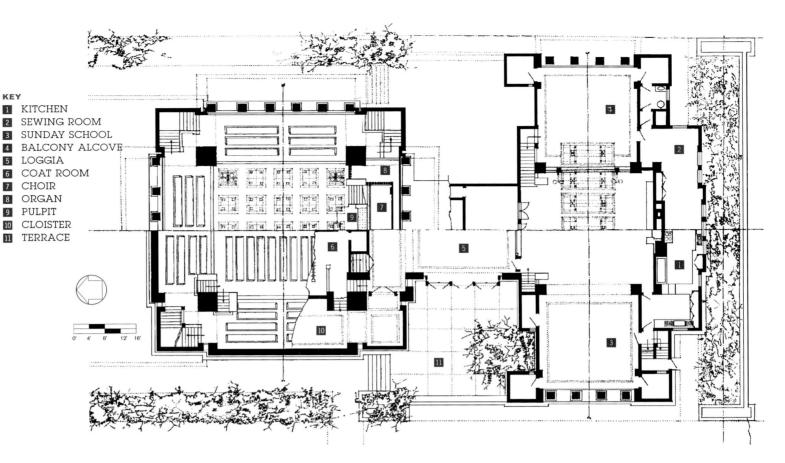

KEY
1. KITCHEN
2. SEWING ROOM
3. SUNDAY SCHOOL
4. BALCONY ALCOVE
5. LOGGIA
6. COAT ROOM
7. CHOIR
8. ORGAN
9. PULPIT
10. CLOISTER
11. TERRACE

Unity Temple (church) plan, composite of three levels

ABOVE The plan of Unity Temple shows clearly how Wright divided the building into two sections, linked by a central entrance loggia. To the left is the church itself – different sections of the plan indicate the long pews and the square skylights above. To the right is Unity House, with its spaces for the Sunday school and other activities.

Order and light

Inside Unity Temple itself there is more warmth and beauty. This does not come from ornament, which is restrained, but from proportions and light. The proportions of the interior derive from a carefully worked-out series of squares, cubes and double cubes, creating a sense of balance and order. The light comes mainly from above – from a grid of square skylights and strips of high clerestory windows. There is stained glass in these windows, but its colour is very restrained – just enough, in the main, to give a warm tinge of amber to the incoming light. Although Wright rejected the pastor's idea of a church with a spire pointing to heaven, he was happy to let the light from the sky be drawn into the room, and to make it feel like warm sunlight even on a cloudy day. So warm and harmonious is the interior that it is easy to forget, given Wright's extensive use of wooden trim and his specially designed light fittings and furniture, that even here there is a lot of exposed concrete.

The church is a compact space. When seated for worship, no one is far from the pulpit and everyone is close together. The feeling of community is important, and is emphasized too in the other main part of the building, Unity House, which is conceived along more domestic lines, with a fireplace near which parishioners could assemble for meetings, or children could gather for Sunday school.

Wright took great pains with the design of Unity Temple. He said in his autobiography that he went through 34 different studies for the building before he reached the final design. When they got used to their unusual church, the parishioners were grateful, and Unity Temple remains one of Wright's most original and best loved buildings.

RIGHT Special care was paid to the light fittings. They are conceived as a coming together of spheres and cubes that branch out from supports dropping down from the ceiling. Even the tops of the cubic fittings, with their patterns of squares unseen by most of the congregation, were treated with great attention to detail.

Midway Gardens

Like the European pleasure gardens of the 18th and 19th centuries, Midway Gardens was a place where people could go to eat, drink and be entertained indoors and out. It consisted of a series of walls and buildings, mostly elaborately decorated with cast concrete designs and with specially commissioned sculptures, and from every angle it presented to the viewer an enticing array of pavilions, roofs and towers, as if the Aztecs had adapted their architecture to entertainment and play.

Location
Chicago, Illinois

Client
Edward C. Waller Jr

Date
1913 (demolished 1929)

Main materials
Brick, patterned concrete block

In 1910, Wright went on a visit to Europe. He had always been a follower of the theatre and had an interest in music, and he was impressed by the way in which, in countries such as Germany, the arts were made part of outdoor entertainment spaces such as beer gardens and pleasure parks. In 1913 he was given the opportunity to create an American version of this kind of venue, when he was commissioned to design Midway Gardens in Chicago.

High and low culture meet Wright's concept was to bring sophistication to the beer garden by combining eating and drinking with high-quality music. He also wanted the experience to be quintessentially American, so he evolved a decorative style all his own, that drew partly on the art of the ancient pre-Columbian cultures of Mexico.

Midway Gardens combined a five-tiered garden and bandstand with such indoor facilities as a club, a tavern, a restaurant and a dance hall. It was large – filling a 600-foot (185-m) square city block – and lavishly decorated with a series of sculptures, which Wright designed in collaboration with the sculptor Alfonso Iannelli. Their figure sculptures, which became known as Sprites, held various abstract geometric forms such as a cube, an octagon and a triangle. These shapes had symbolic associations for Wright, and – so the architect believed – embodied a kind of geometric 'spell power'.

By combining symbolic sculptures with dance floors, beer-drinking with fine architecture, and a casino with good music, the gardens presented a rich mixture of American culture. In the gardens was another, visually appealing contrast: between the prolific mass-produced concrete – often cast to make decorative surfaces – and the striking, hand-made sculptures of Iannelli. At many levels, Wright was bringing high and low culture together in what he saw as a very democratic and American way.

A grand opening All the signs were that it would prove a success. The opening took place on 27 June 1914, the day before the assassination of Austrian Archduke Franz Ferdinand in Sarajevo began the train of events that led to the First World War. Wright described the scene in his autobiography: 'In a scene unforgettable to all who attended, the architectural scheme and color, form, light, and sound had come alive. Thousands of beautifully dressed women and tuxedoed men thronged the scene. And this scene came upon the beholders as a magic spell. All there moved and spoke as if in a dream. They believed it must be one. Yes. Chicago marveled, acclaimed, approved. And Chicago came back and did the same, marveling again and again and again.'

Dispute and decline The prospects for the gardens looked good, but shadows fell over the success. Wright became embroiled in a dispute with Iannelli over the way the sculptor was credited. Wright described the Sprites as 'designed by Frank Lloyd Wright, executed by A. Janelli', which reduced the sculptor's role and added insult to injury by spelling his name incorrectly. Iannelli insisted that he had a key creative role; Wright claimed that the basic ideas were his own and that Iannelli's role was more that of a craftsman than a creative artist.

But more damaging than this dispute was that the owners, who had lacked sufficient ready capital to build the gardens, found that the takings after opening were not enough for them to pay their way. By 1916 they were in receivership, and the gardens passed into other hands. They declined until Prohibition put an end to the kind of entertainment offered there, and they were finally demolished in 1929. A unique masterpiece of architecture and garden planning was lost to Chicago and the world.

OPPOSITE Sculptures by Iannelli guarded the street frontages of the gardens complex, looking down from plinths on top of carefully crafted brick walls. Posters advertise the fact that the gardens are now open, their proprietors no doubt hopeful that a large audience would gather there to be entertained. Sadly, after the first rush of interest, the hope was not fulfilled.

ABOVE Automobiles throng in front of one of the flat-roofed pavilions that made up the main structures in Midway Gardens. These pavilions, similar to those at Tokyo's Imperial Hotel, were covered with abstract decoration, which both architect and client felt was appropriate to buildings associated with a venue devoted to pleasure and entertainment.

LEFT An early colour postcard shows the front of the hotel, with the name in both Japanese and western scripts to appeal to an international market. Cards such as this helped to spread the fame of the hotel after it had survived the devastating earthquake of September 1923 largely undamaged.

BELOW To each side of the lobby block (to the left in this picture) were the long ranges of buildings containing the hotel's guest rooms, which were accessed from central corridors. Some of the rooms looked out on the pool, others on to inner courtyards or the surrounding streets.

Imperial Hotel

Tokyo's Imperial Hotel, in a prominent position near the Imperial Palace, was one of Frank Lloyd Wright's largest projects. With its long wings of bedrooms and its large public rooms – often encrusted with ornament, like the triple-height grand lobby – it was one of the Japanese capital's landmark buildings. The hotel was all the more remarkable because Wright found a way of making it earthquake-proof.

Location
Tokyo, Japan

Client
Hotel management on behalf of Japanese imperial family

Date
1914–22
(demolished 1968)

Main materials
Poured concrete, Oya stone (soft lava block)

Japan – its art, culture and architecture – fascinated Frank Lloyd Wright. He visited the country, collected Japanese prints, and analysed the country's buildings. He felt that the Japanese house, typically grounded in the landscape and using local materials, represented an ideal way to build, a way more 'modern' than contemporary Western architecture because its form grew directly from function and materials. So when Wright was given the chance to design a major building in the Japanese capital, Tokyo, he was enthusiastic, and ended up spending several years in the country seeing the job through.

A challenging project
Although both the plan of the hotel and its decorative details in some ways derive from Midway Gardens, this was a highly complex building that took months of planning, as Wright developed his vision of a building that would provide the visitor with a host of visual delights. Wright took pains to make the hotel an enjoyable place to stay. Not for him the broiler-house uniformity of modern hotel design: almost every room was different from all the others.

The earthquake threat
But the challenge that exercised Wright more than any other was how to cope with the threat of earthquakes. Wright examined the geology of the site and found that it did not help him by offering any kind of solid support. Beneath the topsoil were 60 feet (18 m) of subsoil, with no bedrock within reach. Wright described it graphically as 'eight feet of cheese-like soil that overlay … liquid mud'.

The solution seemed to be to 'float' the building on the mud rather than trying to find some hard foundation for it. In order to do this, Wright designed a series of concrete 'pins' that sank 9 feet (3 m) into the soil. The floor slabs of the building were supported on these pins and cantilevered out from them. The idea was that the building above could move about independently of these pins, coming back to rest on them again once an earthquake was over. In addition, the building was laid out in relatively small sections, with expansion joints in between.

Wright's clients were far from confident that this construction system would work. They insisted that the architect stay in Tokyo for the entire period of construction, and so Wright remained in Tokyo until 1921, watching the building rise, and fending off doubts about his construction methods. He was saved by an earth tremor that hit the hotel when it was under construction. The building shook but stayed in one piece – or rather in its various, independently shifting component pieces – and Wright won new respect as a result.

Telling details
Wright's time in Tokyo meant that he oversaw all the details of the building – the fittings and fixtures, which he had designed, were made and installed under his supervision, making the vast complex a very pure Frank Lloyd Wright building. The overwhelming impression of the ornament is that of a Mayan temple, but the scale of the guest rooms, doors, fittings and spaces is smaller, and more Japanese. Peter Blake, a writer who saw the building, described the attention to scale in his book on Wright: '… in some of the rooms the glazed doors leading out to little balconies are hardly more than five feet high; elsewhere, windows overlooking gardens and courts are so low that one must get down on all fours to enjoy the view.'

The ultimate test
The acid test of the building came dramatically in the great earthquake of 1923. Large parts of the capital were flattened, 100,000 people lost their lives, but out of the confusion Wright received a telegram from the hotel's chairman, Baron Okura: 'HOTEL STANDS UNDAMAGED AS MONUMENT OF YOUR GENIUS HUNDREDS OF HOMELESS PROVIDED FOR BY PERFECTLY MAINTAINED SERVICE CONGRATULATIONS'. The Imperial Hotel lasted another 40 years, and was finally demolished in 1968. It fell in the end not because of earth tremors but because of the pressures of economics, when developers saw they could make money out of a high-rise building on the site.

FRANK LLOYD WRIGHT'S first great creative period lasted from about 1901 to 1910. This was the decade during which he designed a stunning series of buildings known as the 'Prairie Houses'. These houses are not on the Prairies, but would be at home there – they are low houses with strong horizontal emphasis in the design; they seem to reach out into the landscape, and have many porches and balconies, allowing house and landscape to merge; they have views out in many different directions; and they have cantilevered roofs that, like the porches, stretch out to embrace the garden.

Wright planned many of his Prairie Houses using a grid. He had seen this method used in Japanese architecture, where the floor plan of a house would be based on multiples of the standard 6 foot x 3 foot (2 m x 1 m) tatami mat. Wright used grids (sometimes of rectangles, sometimes of squares) in a similar way: the size of the grid would determine not only the dimensions of the floor, but also the size of windows and the distance between elements such as wall timbers. It was a useful design discipline but could also save money when based, as it sometimes was, on the size of standard building components.

Although based on squares, however, Prairie Houses were rarely square in plan. Many had cross-shaped footprints, or plans based on the 'pinwheel' (a kind of cross with offset arms). In a typical cross plan, each arm would house a main room (living room, dining room, kitchen and entry, for example), while the hearth, the heart of all Wright's houses, was placed at the centre. A particular advantage of this kind of plan was that a room occupying a complete arm of the cross had views in three directions, making it light, sun-filled, and – crucially for Wright – giving a range of views of the garden and landscape. This unity of inside and outside, of house and site, was a key feature of what Wright came to call 'organic architecture'.

THE PRAIRIE
HOUSE AND
BEYOND

ABOVE Built quite close to the sidewalk, the Hardy House makes a strong impression with its bold black-and-white outlines and simple rectangular form. Low walls on either side, rendered pale like the walls of the house itself, give the owners privacy in their garden, with its views of nearby Lake Michigan.

The influence of Japan

The Japanese influence is made very clear in a drawing of the house by Wright's associate Marion Mahony, in which the building is seen from below the balcony and framed by the outlines of the surrounding trees and shrubs. The house is portrayed in relation to its environment, and the style of the drawing, with its stylized trees and creative use of white space, owes a lot to the Japanese prints that Wright loved. There is something Japanese too in the strong vertical lines of the house – the window uprights of the lakeside elevation and the vertical timbers of the street frontage, which stand out against the white walls. The architectural writer and scholar Vincent Scully Jr, in his book about the architect, wrote that the house was 'rendered by Wright as an incident in a Japanese screen'. Others have seen both the 'timber-framed' effect of the walls and the use of leaded glass in the windows as drawing on the Japanese influence.

The drawing, no less than the house itself, shows how Wright liked to create drama from his architecture. There is something playful about the way the building clings to its bluff above the lake and something defiant about the way the house stands out from its more conventional neighbours on the street. The locals could not fail to notice this, of course, and most of them were amused by the strange-looking building that had risen in their midst. Some took to laughing at it, maybe sensing something alien and un-American in this odd cuckoo in its Midwestern nest. Perhaps this was why Wright built little in this city in his native state until, more than two decades later, he began work on his buildings for Johnson Wax (see pages 112–115).

As usual with Wright, the details in the house are as interesting and meticulous as the planning and massing. One example of this care over detail is the windows. Like many Wright houses, the Thomas Hardy House has windows containing the art glass that the architect was so fond of. Narrow strips of coloured glass, made of patterns of rectangles and squares held together with 'leading' that is actually made of zinc, are arranged around the edges of each opening. They make an elegant 'frame within the window frame'. The owners of the Racine property have looked after these windows with care – something of a challenge because the house is sited so close to the sidewalk and some years ago vandals began to smash some of the glass. The owners responded with a pragmatic solution – covering the glazing in protective clear plastic sheeting. This reduces the glittering effect of the art glass from outside, but has done a good job of protecting the precious material.

Robie House
60

Robie House

The Robie House is the ultimate Prairie House. Its finely crafted 'Roman' brick walls and perfectly balanced cantilevered roofs are as stunning and well composed as an abstract painting by Mondrian. The overhanging roofs are also artful in another way, shading the house at midday, but letting in plenty of light when and where it is needed. The house is a masterpiece of both style and substance.

Location
Chicago, Illinois

Client
Frederick C. Robie

Date
1906

Main materials
Brick, steel

'I know what you want – one of those damn Wright houses.' Frederick C. Robie was an inventor and manufacturer – of automobile and bicycle parts – who had 'made it'. A practical man who knew what he wanted, he jotted down his ideas for the kind of house he needed for himself, his wife and their young family. When he showed his ideas to builders, that brusque response was the one that stuck in his mind. So he went to see Wright, and they got on.

A modern house

Robie wanted a modern house, which for him meant two things: first, it would be a clutter-free dwelling in a modern architectural idiom; second, it would be full of the latest technology. The builders who Robie consulted knew that Frank Lloyd Wright was the man who could deliver on these requirements. And so it proved. Wright was at his most creative when responding to Robie's requests, designing perhaps the greatest of all his Prairie Houses.

Space and place

Spatially the house is remarkable. The Wright hallmarks are refined and expanded to striking effect. Long roofs are cantilevered far out over the porches and balconies, hovering above them with little visible means of support, and providing shelter and protection from glare. Large living rooms are glazed with the architect's usual lavishness, opening the house to the garden. The main living room is on the upper floor – set above the children's playroom and the billiard room – so benefiting from good views and plenty of light.

The house is artfully positioned on its lot. The local standard was to set back the buildings some 35 feet (11 m) from the sidewalk. This went against the instincts of Wright, who liked to build as near to the street as he could, as if his houses were reaching out to embrace arriving visitors. He solved the dilemma by respecting the building line with the main walls, but throwing out both his cantilevered roofs and the garden wall beyond it, so that the house seemed to extend right up to the sidewalk. Naturally, the garden wall is built of the same 'Roman' brick – topped and tailed with pale masonry, as the rest of the house – so that it 'reads' as part of the structure.

Structure and technology

As this structure went up, onlookers watched in amazement. Although from the outside the house looks like a brick building, the structural heart of it is the steelwork: long beams that support the magically cantilevered roofs.

LEFT In strong sunlight, the Robie House shows its impressive design to best advantage, with its brick walls bathed in light and the huge overhanging roofs in contrasting shadow. The long row of windows lets in plenty of natural light to the living and dining rooms, while the porches provide shade, giving Frederick C. Robie the best of both worlds.

RIGHT A view from the front deck shows the fine brickwork, its horizontal mortar courses clearly emphasized, that makes up the walls of the Robie House. Planters are integrated into the stone coping at some points, to bring nature close to this suburban house.

KEY

1 PORCH   6 BATH   11 FIRE
2 LIVING   7 KITCHEN
3 DINING   8 SERVANT'S DINING
4 BALCONY   9 SERVANT
5 GUEST   10 CORRIDOR

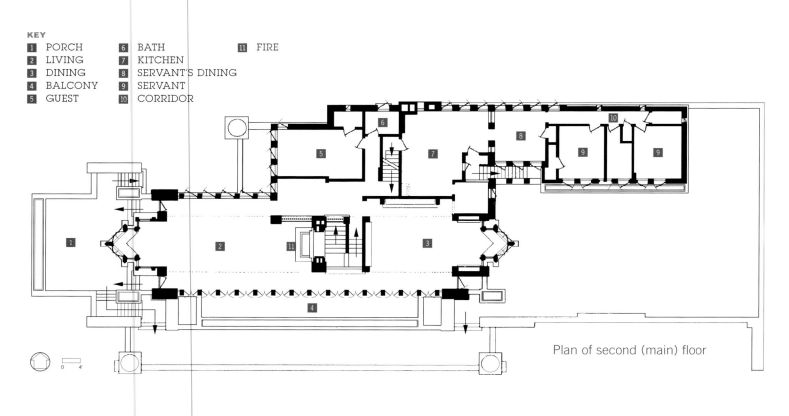

Plan of second (main) floor

Even those who passed the site regularly, watching as the beams were bolted together, were impressed by the sheer length of the cantilevers, made possible by the structure. With its long lines and vast 'decks', it was one of those houses that make people think of an ocean liner. It, and Wright, were clearly going places.

If the planning is everything we have come to expect of Wright, the technology was even more so. The house benefited from the best and latest in electric lighting (with fittings designed by Wright), burglar and fire alarms, the most up-to-date telephones and an industrial-type vacuum-cleaning system. Robie the inventor was satisfied, as he no doubt was by the commodious triple garage for his automobiles.

It all cost a lot, even if, at around $60,000, it was a fraction of the price of the Darwin Martin House. But there were no disagreements between client and architect about the budget this time. Robie knew he was creating something special, and had confidence in Wright's ability to produce it. Perhaps it was because both men, in their different ways, were innovators and engineers and could admire one another's skill. Both knew too that this kind of innovation rarely comes cheap.

The clients and their house
By all accounts, the Robies were happy with their house. If Frederick liked the technology and the space, his wife responded positively to the lightness, the garden, and the space provided for the children. But they were not destined to live long in their architectural masterpiece. Within two years of moving in, the couple were divorced, Robie having cheated on his wife. The house was sold.

Robie's troubles did not end there. Soon his father died, leaving vast debts, which the son – a man of honour in his financial dealings, at least – felt he should pay off. The cost of this wiped out Robie's fortune and he never recovered financially. The house survived, however, even though it lost some of its features, such as the wall that screened off the garage court. Much of the furniture that Wright designed specially for the house has gone too, depriving the interiors of the coherence they once had. On its Chicago street, surrounded by other buildings, it does rather look like a Prairie House that has travelled a long way from its natural home. But it is still one of Wright's greatest buildings, a testimony to what can happen when architect and client share a clear and radical vision.

ABOVE The plan of the main floor of the Robie House is surprisingly simple. The two main living rooms with the stairs between them make up one long rectangle. An adjoining rectangle of a similar size houses the service accommodation and a guest room. Beyond these blocks, the balcony and porch that give the house its striking character extend to the south and west.

OPPOSITE TOP The main part of the dining room is reserved for a large table with high-backed chairs, but beyond there is a more intimate space, an inglenook with a pointed bay window. It was important in a large house to provide smaller, more private spaces as well as large rooms for entertaining.

OPPOSITE BOTTOM The living room is one of Wright's lightest. The French windows on the left open on to the balcony overlooking the street. The windows in the centre lead to the large, shady porch. There are yet more windows out of shot to the right. At night, two long rows of spherical lamps flood the room with light.

LEFT The art glass in the Robie House windows is both intricate and beautiful. The patterns are made up of a complex mixture of diamonds, triangles, parallelograms and other shapes. Wright liked to integrate the decoration into his designs in this way, scorning such decorative add-ons as wallpaper.

Coonley House

Set in its estate in Riverside, Illinois, the Coonley House is a vast building, sprawling among gardens, courtyards and trees. The large complex, including a gardener's cottage and stables (now converted to a separate dwelling), is unified visually by the use of pale walls, dark window frames and shallow pitched roofs. The interiors are impressive, too: dominated by their many windows and skylights and big, pitched, timber-framed ceilings, giving a generous sense of height and space.

Location
Riverside, Illinois

Client
Avery Coonley and
Queene Ferry Coonley

Date
1907

Main materials
Brick, glass

Avery Coonley was a graduate of Harvard and MIT who worked in his family's business for a few years before devoting himself to his philanthropic interests, to his passion for education and to Christian Science. His wife, Queene, a member of the rich Ferry family, had studied education and shared her husband's interests. The couple were also devoted to the arts and entertained on a lavish and formal scale.

The importance of 'principle' When the Coonleys
decided to build themselves a house, they took time to look at many recent houses, including a number designed by Wright – they probably went to an exhibition including his work in the Art Institute of Chicago. Wright's work attracted them strongly, Mrs Coonley saying that they found in it 'the countenances of principle'. As Christian Scientists the Coonleys believed that if something were based on sound principles then its execution would be sound too. This was therefore a compliment and Wright was understandably pleased. He resolved to do his best for the Coonleys and they put their considerable fortune at his disposal.

The house that Wright built for Coonley was one of his largest. Unlike many of the Prairie Houses, it is a courtyard building in which the living accommodation and service buildings are arranged in a U-shape around a central garden area. The house is 'zoned' – in other words, different parts of the 'U' contain rooms of different functions: living rooms in one section, service rooms in another, bedrooms and guest rooms in the third. Unlike the traditional courtyard house, the principal rooms have their main outlook not over the courtyard but over the surrounding grounds, into which the rambling house sprawls. The low-slung design is enhanced with typical Wright touches such as leaded-glass windows, specially designed lamps and – a new departure for Wright – polychrome tiles. So the Coonley House is an outward-looking building that marries the courtyard and Prairie House principles. This is a successful marriage, and Wright was proud of the house, rating it his favourite when he wrote his autobiography – although at that point many of his greatest houses, such as Fallingwater, had yet to be built.

Interior spaces The Coonley House is a grand house for
a rich client, but it does not have a grand entrance. The door is hidden away in a rather shadowy spot under a porch. This is not unusual with Wright: he is not often an architect of showy doorways. He was more interested in what happened as you entered the building, in the process of discovering the house. So at the Coonley House, the visitor enters in the shadows and walks up three steps to a landing. From here a stairway goes up to the next floor, where the main reception rooms are located. Ascending the stair, you walk into the

OPPOSITE This façade of the large Coonley House looks modest – the pale range of buildings does not look as if it is part of a big house. With his keen sense of the theatrical, Wright sometimes liked to surprise visitors to his houses, building a simple frontage or small entry that leads to much larger and more impressive spaces.

RIGHT The Coonley living room has a much more impressive exterior, on which several elements – such as the uprights between the windows and the ironwork – are richly patterned. In the foreground is one of the planters that Wright used on many of his houses, a round bowl set in a square surround.

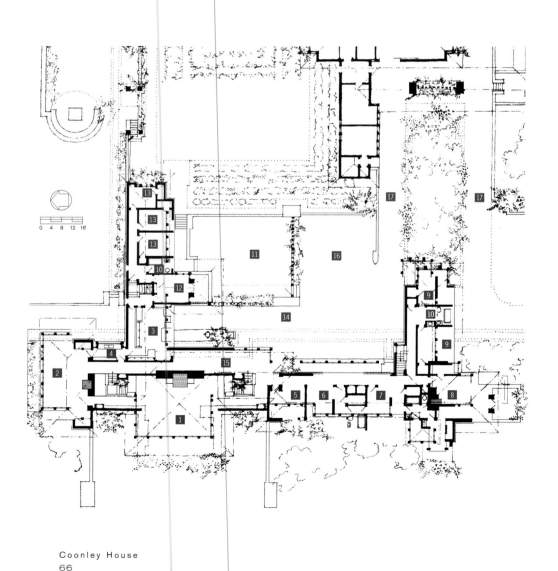

Main floor plan

KEY
1 LIVING
2 DINING
3 KITCHEN
4 PANTRY
5 STUDY
6 BED
7 CHILDREN'S BED
8 PARENTS' BED
9 GUEST BED
10 BATH
11 SERVANT'S COURT
12 SERVANT
13 MAID
14 DRIVE
15 HALL
16 COURT
17 INCLINED DRIVE

light, for, in contrast to the rather dark lower floor, the main rooms are beautifully lit. So you are drawn along, first towards the dining room (lit by windows on three sides), then down a skylit gallery to the living room, another light and imposing space. Again, this room is lit by windows on three sides. The fourth side houses the fireplace, with its long mural of forest scenery – fern and birch designs in autumnal colours – on either side, so that there is a sense of the landscape enveloping the room, both in the form of the real scenery glimpsed through the windows and of the trees in the mural.

Because these main rooms are on the upper floor of the house, the first floor is little more than a basement and the playroom is the only important room on this lower floor. The living rooms therefore command good views over the garden. Wright filled these living rooms with specially designed furniture. Even the carpet on the living room-floor was made especially to the architect's design, and he made sure that the pattern in the carpet, which was handmade in Austria, reflected the designs of other details in the house.

The later history of the house

The Coonleys lived in their house until they moved to Washington DC in 1917, when Avery Coonley was invited to do public relations and lobbying work for the Church of Christ Scientist in the District of Columbia. He died in Washington in 1920, but his wife lived for another 38 years, and did not forget Wright. When the architect, like so many other Americans, fell on hard times in the late 1920s, she was one of the group of clients who rallied round, paid off his debts and saved him financially.

In the 1950s an architect and developer called Arnold Skrow bought the property and split it up, making two separate homes out of the huge house and turning the stable and gardener's cottage into separate dwellings too. It was a compromise, but one that allowed Wright's great house to survive. Although still subdivided, it is now in the hands of caring owners.

Meyer May House

A compact building in tan brick with pitched red-tiled roofs, the Meyer May House is an example of the way Frank Lloyd Wright could create a near-perfect design with limited means. The small details – such as the copper roof-trim, the art-glass windows, and the specially made furniture – make this an outstanding example of the small Prairie House.

Location
Grand Rapids, Michigan
Client
Meyer May
Date
1908
Main materials
Brick, glass

Businessman Meyer May, who had made his money in the clothing business, came to Wright in 1908 for a house for himself, his wife Sophie and their two adopted children. For many, the house Wright produced was one of his best. It is not a large building, but in its design the architect managed to marry his aesthetic flair with a practical approach that made the place comfortable and good to live in. Thanks to a particularly happy restoration in 1987–8, it is once more a perfect Wright house, a beautifully crafted example of Wright's special blend of traditional and modern, standing out like an architectural beacon among the more conventional houses in the neighbourhood.

Tricks of design The exterior is dominated by sweeping cantilevered roofs. Some of these roofs overhang so much that it seems amazing that they do not fall down under the weight of Michigan's winter snows. Wright was sailing close to the wind here and risking structural damage or collapse, an issue that was finally resolved when the house was restored in the 1980s. There is no faulting the detailing, though. Copper trim lines the roofs and its colour is picked up in the window frames, giving the outside a feeling of harmony. For the brickwork, Wright used his trick of emphasizing the horizontal mortar joints by raking them out and using darker mortar. The effect is to draw subtle horizontal lines around the building, something that the casual visitor hardly notices, but which helps suggest subliminally that the building is low and horizontal.

Entering the house entails experiencing another typical Wright trick – the hidden, dark entryway that leads into main living rooms flooded with light. The first of these rooms is the dining room, which is dominated by the Wright-designed dining table. At its corners stand four large light standards, each with a stained-glass shade on top of a tall wooden pedestal. They spread warm light over the table and make a very effective statement from wherever you sit or stand. This is not a large room, but the layout and furnishing make it imposing – no doubt the Mays' friends were impressed when they sat down for a meal.

Decorative effects
The other main space, the living room, is focused on the fireplace. Here Wright emphasized the horizontal mortar courses not with darker mortar but with an inlay of brightly shining glass or tile. This catches the light – during the day from the numerous windows and skylights, and at night from the fire itself – and makes the fireplace shimmer. A simple effect, it gives the room a memorable richness of texture, which is enhanced by the art glass in the windows and by the strong patterning in the window glazing bars.

Further decorative effects come from the work of Milwaukee interior specialist George Niedecken, who collaborated with Wright on many of his houses, creating furniture and murals to the architect's specifications. A delightful hollyhock mural by Niedecken is a notable feature in the Meyer May House.

Upstairs, the bedrooms are simpler. Wright pragmatically held that rich decoration was not so important in rooms in which people spent most of their time asleep. So, with the exception of some more glittering glass inserted in the mortar around the fireplace in the master bedroom, simple finishes are the order of the day. The rich woods of furniture, floors and other fittings provide all the colour that is needed. The sloping ceilings provide added spatial interest.

Restoration
For some time, though, Wright's unified vision for this fine house was compromised. Over the years the house was extended, and by the 1980s it was looking the worse for wear and a far cry from the structure Wright designed. Fortunately for Wright's legacy, however, the building was purchased

LEFT The Meyer May House is one of those in which there is only minimal masonry on the upper floor, which is lit by strips of windows. The resulting lack of upper walls makes the roof seem to float above the house. This view shows the terrace, with the living and dining rooms behind. The entrance is hidden away at the other side of the house.

RIGHT The details on this Prairie House are particularly carefully worked, as this photograph of the living room French windows shows. Wright seems to have relished the combination of copper cladding and light brown brickwork, designing more complex window openings than usual, the rectangles reflecting the smaller patterns in the art glass.

by Steelcase Inc., the office furniture company that produced the furnishings for Wright's Johnson Wax buildings (see pages 112–115). Steelcase set about restoring the house. Aiming to bring the building back to the way it looked when it was new, the restorers demolished the extension. Setting to work on Wright's vision, they researched the architect's original plans and drawings, and compared them with his other designs and extant buildings. Gradually the house was repaired, and one structural issue – the daring cantilevered roof – was addressed with the insertion of more supportive steelwork. Now the weight of the roof, and the winter snow load, are supported as never before.

The original decorations were restored, and the house was furnished with a mixture of original pieces, reproduction Wright furniture and compatible items in the Arts and Crafts style from around the time it was built. The house is now open to the public so that visitors and students can appreciate the architect's achievement. The restored building is a powerful tribute to the master's capacity for taking pains.

Coonley Playhouse

This small building is in the grounds of the house that Frank Lloyd Wright built for Avery and Queene Coonley in Riverside, Illinois. An elegant structure on a cross-shaped plan with pale walls and flat roofs, it is an impressive exercise in solid forms and planes, a design that is more important and impressive than its small size suggests. An unusual project for Wright, it was built as a small school, but has subsequently been converted for residential use.

Location
Riverside, Illinois

Client
Queene Ferry Coonley

Date
1911

Main materials
Concrete, glass

Avery Coonley and his wife Queene Ferry Coonley were among Wright's richest clients. When they had settled in the large house in Riverside, Illinois that Wright designed for them (see pages 64–67), they began to plan a new building, reflecting their interest in education.

School and stage
As Christian Scientists, the Coonleys had strong beliefs about education and the bringing up of their daughter. Avery Coonley was also a director of *The Dial*, a political and literary magazine that was published in Chicago but gained a national reputation for its discussions of books, writers, and trends in politics. But the Coonleys' involvement was also on a more practical level than this. Queene Coonley was an experienced and qualified teacher and started a small 'cottage school' for her daughter and a number of other children in the neighbourhood. They commissioned Wright to design a school building near their Riverside house.

Because it has a stage and has been used for theatrical performances, the structure is now known as the Coonley Playhouse. It is a pale-walled building, its predominantly light colour relieved at the front by three strong vertical bands of glazing. There are flat roofs, which overhang in several directions, providing shade, and trees and shrubs have grown up around the walls, softening its lines and making it rise from the garden more organically than it must have done when it first appeared, new and white, in 1911–12.

OPPOSITE Outside, the trio of big windows, the overhanging roofs and the large central block with its smaller flanking wings set up a satisfying composition of shapes and forms. This highly linear building is saved from looking stark by the way it blends in with the surrounding trees.

RIGHT The glass in the Playhouse windows is rather different from Wright's usual art glass – the balloon-like circles and primary colours seem just right for a building used by children. The design has proved very popular and is now licensed for use on all kinds of objects, from lamps to wall clocks.

This is a small building but many have admired its flair and elegance, and books and articles about Wright have given it more prominence than one might guess from its small size. Henry-Russell Hitchcock, in his pioneering 1942 book on Wright, refers to the 'virtuosity of poised planes and balanced masses' demonstrated on the building's exterior, while finding the interior rather heavier and more 'architectural'. He rightly finds similarities between this building and the pavilions of Wright's large Midway Gardens scheme – both, in their different ways, were buildings connected with culture and entertainment. Hitchcock also admires the way in which Wright tried to create an identity of scale inside and outside the building.

The Playhouse is not a theatre in the conventional meaning of the term, but because the Coonleys were interested in the theatre, and believed that it should be an element in their child's education, the interior of the school was built with a raised area at one end, which could be used as a stage.

Balloons and confetti windows
The Coonley Playhouse is a cruciform building lit by tall windows at one end and high, clerestory windows on either side. Its main space is the school assembly room. Wright decorated its windows with charming art-glass designs in strong primary colours, using a motif known as 'balloons and confetti'. This design may have been inspired by a similar one in the floor of the Petit Palais in Paris, which Wright would probably have seen when he visited the French capital in 1910. Although the Playhouse is now a residence, some of these windows can still be seen in New York's Museum of Modern Art; others are now privately owned. The windows have also provided the inspiration for various commercially available objects, including jewellery, cups and plates.

Reproductions of the original clerestory windows were made and fitted during the late 1980s. These have been made of white glass with a very thin layer of colour applied to the surface. William Allin Storrer, in *The Architecture of Frank Lloyd Wright: A Complete Catalog*, has explained the significance of this technique and the difference from conventional stained glass: 'This allows the glass to appear plain outside during the day, yet the design inside is brightly colored; stained glass would be visible outside and would not be as bright inside. At night, the pattern is visible outside, but appears as pastel color; with stained glass, the color would be bright outside at night'. This beautiful glass helped turn a rather severe pale box of a building into something richer – a schoolroom that must have been both appealing and stimulating to the children who learned and played there.

Taliesin

Taliesin has become synonymous with Frank Lloyd Wright. Planned as both the architect's home and the base of his architectural practice, it combined these different functions elegantly. But successive fires destroyed parts of the building and would have destroyed the life of a man less determined to carry on than Wright. The architect doggedly rebuilt his home, and much of what survives today is from the 1925 rebuild.

Location
Spring Green, Wisconsin
Client
The architect
Date
1911, 1925
Main materials
Stone, wood, glass

The years 1909 to 1911 saw a crisis in Wright's life. He left his wife Catherine for Mamah Borthwick Cheney, the wife of his Oak Park neighbour and client Edwin Cheney, and eventually left the USA with Mamah Cheney for a year-long stay in Europe. Finding his various assistants unwilling to take over his architectural practice in his absence, Wright left it in the hands of a little-known German architect called Hermann von Holst. When he returned to America in 1911, Wright was faced with the task of rebuilding his Chicago practice. He also decided to build a country house and workplace for himself on land belonging to his mother's family at Spring Green, Wisconsin.

House and hillside Wright called his new house Taliesin, the name of an ancient, possibly mythical British poet. Literally the word means 'shining brow', and no doubt Wright chose it because he built the house on a hillside. The architect himself, though, did not hold with the idea of building a house *on* a hill: '… no house should ever be put *on* a hill or *on* anything. It should be *of* the hill. Belonging to it. Hill and house should live together each the happier for the other.' In the 'organic' architecture that Wright championed, house and landscape should be as one.

The house was planned in a rather similar way to Wright's house for Avery Coonley, although on a much less grand scale. Like the Coonley House, Taliesin had a courtyard and the buildings were arranged around it in a U-shape. At each end was a large wing: one containing the main house, the other a service area with stables, garages and a cowshed. Connecting these two wings was a narrow building containing a long workroom and a loggia. This loggia was a key feature because it was the way through which you entered the house and it provided a stunning view over the valley before you turned into the entrance hall.

The building was to be one that Wright continuously modified and rebuilt. But although there were many changes and expansions, natural materials – stone walls, cedar shingles, woollen rugs – were always predominant and gave a sense of continuity. Many of the stone walls are left unplastered inside the house, heightening the sense of unity between interior and exterior. And this unity is further enhanced by the use of stone in the garden. From the living room, you look out past stone interior walls to stone outer walls, and towards garden walls and paths also made of stone.

From the beginning, this house, grounded in the Wisconsin countryside, meant many things to Wright. It was planned as a home and workplace away from the city – a place where he could live in tranquillity

RIGHT Beautifully set at the top of a slope, Taliesin is designed to provide its occupants with good views – but also to dominate the hillside where it sits. Yet this building, for all its size and dominance, does not seem imposed on the slope but appears to emerge from it, its outline broken up and softened by the surrounding trees.

OPPOSITE The dining room is a
simple space, dominated by the
large Wright-designed table and
chairs; but the architect, as usual,
took great care with the details.
There is a pleasing combination of
surfaces – including wood, stone,
plaster and glass – together with
an artful use of different planes,
especially the various slopes of
the ceiling.

with Mamah Cheney, somewhere from which he could draw inspiration from a landscape of rare beauty, a base for his group of apprentices, and also a place where he could connect with his mother's Wisconsin ancestry.

A media firestorm

Wright and Cheney did not achieve their hoped-for tranquillity, however. They created a furore, and Wright himself, while claiming he wanted to be left in peace, fanned the flames of a media fire. The couple moved to Taliesin in 1911, and Wright – getting wind of public disapproval of his relationship with Cheney – called a defiant press conference on Christmas Day to justify his conduct.

It was an extraordinary and badly timed action, and when the press arrived the architect read out a self-justifying statement attempting to explain his actions. He asked the reporters to give him a chance, to 'go slow in deciding that he [had] acted badly'; but the newspapers showed no mercy, denouncing Wright for deserting his children on Christmas Day, of all days.

Instead of letting the fire die down, Wright retaliated and issued a written statement, couched in somewhat pompous prose, offering further justifications. He claimed that his first marriage had been the mistake of a young man, that he loved Mamah, that he had had a genuine struggle with his conscience, but that in the end he could only 'carry out life's purpose' with Mamah at his side. In spite of his best efforts, he said, 'the hue and cry of the yellow press was raised, the man and woman defamed'.

Needless to say, the representatives of the 'yellow press' did not take kindly to this description, and the pointless public bickering continued for some days. Eventually, Wright returned to his work, absorbing himself in the commissions that were beginning to come in again, and continuing his emotional commitment to Mamah and to his new house, Taliesin.

Disaster and recovery

But if the architect made a huge emotional investment in the place, this was to be put under the severest strain. In August 1914, when Wright was working in Chicago, a deranged servant armed with a hatchet went on a murderous rampage through the house, killing seven people before setting the place on fire. Much of the residential part of the building was destroyed, only the stone parts surviving the flames. The working part of the house escaped largely unscathed. The dead were William Weston, a favourite carpenter who worked with Wright; an apprentice, Emil Brodelle; workers David Lindblom and Thomas Brunker; and Mamah Cheney and her two children.

Wright was devastated. He had spent five years rebuilding his emotional life, and now everything he had worked for was gone. To add to his pain, he had to cope with the moralizing criticisms of many commentators, who argued that what had happened was just punishment for an adulterous couple. But Wright's Spring Green neighbours were more supportive, and the tragedy seemed to increase Wright's determination to make something of the place. He quickly set about rebuilding the house very much to the original plan.

But this was not the end of the story. In 1925 the house caught fire again, this time as the result of a lightning strike. In the same year, Wright once more began a rebuild, taking the opportunity to make the house larger. The drafting room filled up with apprentices, and life went on in the extended house. With the workroom so crowded, Wright himself usually worked in a small private room, where he had a view of the courtyard and the peace to work on his drawings. In spaces dominated by natural materials such as stone and wood, and looking out over a landscape of Wisconsin countryside and artificial lakes that Wright had dug in the ground, the architect could continue to produce designs for buildings that were 'of' their surroundings and grounded in the American landscape.